DISTANT SUNFLOWER FIELDS

LI JUAN

Translated by
Christopher Payne

SINOIST

Published by
Sinoist Books (Imprint of ACA Publishing Ltd)
University House
11-13 Lower Grosvenor Place,
London SW1W 0EX, UK
Tel: +44 20 3289 3885
E-mail: info@alaincharlesasia.com
Web: www.alaincharlesasia.com

Beijing Office
Tel: +86 (0) 10 8472 1250

Author: Li Juan
Translator: Christopher Payne

**Published by ACA Publishing Ltd in association with the China Translation &
Publishing House**

Original Chinese Text © 遥远的向日葵地 (Yáo Yuǎn De Xiàng Rì Kuí Di) 2017,
Guangdong Flower City Publishing House co., Ltd, Guangdong, China

English Translation © 2021, ACA Publishing Ltd, London, UK

Paperback ISBN: 978-1-83890-506-4
eBook ISBN: 978-1-83890-508-8

A catalogue record for *Distant Sunflower Fields* is available from the National
Bibliographic Service of the British Library.

经典中国国际出版工程
China Classics International

DISTANT SUNFLOWER FIELDS

LI JUAN

Translated by
CHRISTOPHER PAYNE

ACA PUBLISHING LIMITED

A YEAR OF DISASTERS

The Ulungur begins in the east and flows west, extending horizontally through the Altai mountain range to dip at its southern foothills into the Gobi. The land is mostly barren, except for a few bits of stalwart vegetation that cling near to the river, etching a trace of greenery into what is otherwise a blighted landscape. Whatever crops there may be are sown as close to the riverbank as possible. The roads, too, hug the river's path, as do the towns that populate the region, none daring to venture too far from the only source of fresh water. Like metal shavings drawn to a magnet, or people sitting around a campfire, the river drew everything to it. Nothing dared to leave it, or stay very far away from it. It was the only river in the area, and as such the villages and the hungry farm fields would call upon its life-giving energy frequently, perhaps far too frequently. It also flowed through my village, a lonely outpost called Akehala – if only as a much shallower stream. The river was reliant on the weather, as most bodies of water are, and on those occasions when snow fell less than usual, say when a warm winter visited us, it would struggle mightily, reduced to but a trickle of water that barely wetted its riverbed.

In the northern steppes, each and every river relied on melting snow.

But this year had been strangely dry – a rare occurrence. Sort of. If one listened to what people said, the winter snows this past year had hardly reached a third of the normal amount, which didn't bode well for the rest of the year. It wasn't surprising, therefore, that before spring even arrived, local television was already reporting the impending drought.

When it came time to irrigate the fields, endless disputes over water seemed inevitable, so much so that guards had to be posted near the reservoir, pitiful though its reserves may have been.

The dry winter was not the only source of the disastrous year ahead, however, as locusts soon descended on the area, bringing with them even further devastation. The locals blamed it on the mild winter... the lack of bitter cold meant the insect larvae had survived the winter months.

And if that wasn't bad enough, the severe drought conditions exacerbated the already precarious balance between grasslands and the ever-present Gobi, preventing even the smallest shoots of grass from pushing up through the merciless sand. As a result, the wild animals that relied on these grasses soon started migrating north towards the Ulungur River and the villages and people there. Like locusts, they devoured everything they could find. It was, you could say, a perfect storm for farmers who fought on valiantly in the face of such an unforgiving environment.

Yet, this was the year my mum, mostly by herself, set out towards the southern banks of the Ulungur to plant sunflowers... She'd rent ninety acres... a rather small amount.

It was the second year in a row she'd sown these seeds.

Sunflower sprouts are not without enemies. In truth, when they reach up through the ground and grow to about ten centimetres, they become prime targets for the grassland gazelles that range far and wide. For the new bulbs, defeat is preordained, and within a single night, gazelles could tear through acre upon acre of tilled land. That's what they did to Mum. Ninety acres picked nearly clean. In a single night.

It wouldn't be true to say my mum was the only victim of the onslaught as every field far and wide suffered the same fate, but no one was affected as severely as Mum.

Firstly, the land she looked after was at the extreme edge of the ten thousand acres cultivated by the people hanging on in the region, directly adjacent to the sandy wasteland that stretched even further. Secondly, she didn't actually have all that much land – ninety acres was a pittance compared to what most other farmers had – and that had now been devoured.

Other households that had much more land to till, some over a thousand acres, were less affected... After all, no one would pay much attention to a dozen or so acres falling victim to gazelles – but that goes without saying, doesn't it? It's hard to compare...

There was very little Mum could do, other than purchase more seeds and try again.

On her second attempt that year, the weather agreed a little more, and there was even some rain, so the soil wasn't half as bad. It didn't take long for the newly planted crop to burst through the ground, much faster than the first time. But no sooner had her ninety acres turned a lush green than they were picked clean again in the span of one night.

Mum was obstinate. Stubborn. She clenched her teeth and tried for a third time. It didn't take long, however, for the most recent crop to meet the same fate as the first two. What can I say? Mum was thoroughly heartbroken. Dejected. And at a loss as to whom she should air her grievances.

That's when she learned that the wild animals repeatedly ravaging her land fell under the forestry department's jurisdiction. There was, in her mind, someone to blame, so she took off as quickly as she could to lodge a formal complaint.

Unfortunately, the reception she received upon entering the forestry department's offices in the regional capital was cool and unwelcoming. They promised compensation, yes, but no sooner had the promise been made than they asked for proof, for evidence of what had happened.

"Evidence?" Mum asked. "What the devil do you mean?"

She told me about his response. He needed a photo... a picture of the animals actually eating her crops… He smiled as he told her. Needless to say, rage bubbled to the surface of my mother's face. She was a poor farmer, and all she carried on her person was a spade and the seeds she would plant. How in hell would she have a camera with her? Who in their right mind would bring a camera out into the fields? Certainly no farmer. And besides, Mum thought while the man was smiling at her, those bastard little animals were quick as a flash and made hardly any sound at all… The briefest of human movement and *poof*, they'd be off, disappearing over the horizon. Take a picture of them in the act, their snouts driving into the earth, ravenously consuming her sunflower seeds? She'd need a telescope or binoculars for that… and a bloody good camera too!

It couldn't be anything else but a lost year.

And yet, this didn't stop her from trying a fourth time.

What we call 'hope', 'perseverance'… the energy and hard work we put into it… Perhaps it is stronger than complete despair… if only by a little bit.

To be fair, the gazelles, too, should be pitied. They weren't being vindictive in their repeated attacks on my mother's field. They were starving – the weather had seen to that. And to them, the land had no boundaries beyond which they could walk. There were no lines on a map, and they didn't pay any heed to supposed ownership. During the day, when humans were about, they'd simply roam back and forth on the edges of the fields, their stomachs empty and aching, until such time they spied, usually in the distance, a bit of greenery to the north. Then, when night fell, they would edge closer and closer, silently, stealthily, and then they'd plunge their mouths into the dirt, eating what they could, their ears cocked and at attention…

Their lives were as bitter as those of the people who lived out here. After all, the tilled fields and the vegetation that grew there didn't really compare to the wild grasses they were used to. For one, they weren't bunched together but rather spaced almost equal distances apart. This meant there were far fewer of the sunflower sprouts than the grasses of the grassland, at least in normal times. In fact, ninety acres would hardly fill their bellies.

Unsurprisingly, some of the beasts would still be sniffing about the fields when morning dawned, scrounging for what little bit of food there was. The farmers who saw this naturally flew into crazy fits of rage, quickly jumping into whatever vehicle they had and immediately giving chase. In response, the animals would take off running, desperately trying to outpace the much more dangerous mechanical creature. But rarely would they succeed in escaping. The farmers were, after all, relentless and revengeful. They'd run down the gazelles, literally in some cases, and soon the brave stragglers from the night before would be dead, their lungs exploded from the chase, or their bodies crushed under the wheels.

But where does human life go from here? How does it find better days? Spring had passed, and now the expanse of fields, the ten thousand acres, still remained barren and empty.

With these thoughts weighing on her, Mum's fourth attempt met an altogether different, and much better, fate.

As the summer rolled into July, the gazelles faced their own trial, and after that they were not seen again.

Where had they gone? Had water grasses suddenly appeared? Had they discovered some untouched and bountiful land, some hidden paradise lush and green? On the surface, the steppe seemed to stretch for as far as the eye could see, but in truth there were knotted and somewhat luxuriant forests nestled here and there, groves of trees that were adept at concealing myriad things...

Whatever the case may have been for the gazelles, in the end Mum's fourth attempt was a success, even if she couldn't explain how or why. The sunflowers grew strong and vigorous, full of life. It was their first time to greet the world.

2

CHOUCHOU AND SAIHU

At nearly the same time, Chouchou came into this world, all four paws of him. He must've been about three months old when he appeared out of the quiet wasteland. Mum took him in almost immediately, and he never ventured far from her side after that. So much so in fact that each and every day I would only ever see her and Chouchou, along with Saihu, a smaller dog we had had for a while, and the chickens, ducks, geese and rabbits... as well as the growing sunflowers which seemed to reach further into the sky all the time. There was really nothing else.

I think it was because of this absence of anything else that when the gazelles first appeared they came as an enormous shock to Chouchou's world!

Upon seeing them, he would bark and go wild, running back and forth as though he were a rabid beast, causing his own amount of destruction, it must be said, to the sunflower fields themselves. Before long, a great dust cloud arose in his wake, obscuring him and the gazelles. It was really quite the scene.

On the steppe, we all called the gazelles 'yellow sheep', despite the fact that they were much larger. Their body shape, too, was more akin to a deer than a lamb. But the name stuck. I don't know why. They were tallish creatures, slim and with a certain kind of vigorousness that no sheep ever had; they were much nimbler and more surefooted, too. You could even say they were shrewd in a way, especially with how they acted towards people. I mean, there was a strong, almost intimidating explosiveness about them whenever they sensed danger, and when they did run there was little that anyone could do to catch them, unless they had a vehicle close by. Indeed, the gazelles galloped like grassland horses more than anything else.

But Chouchou didn't seem to care at all, or he was unafraid at least, for he would still chase after the animals with a ferociousness more akin to a wolf, his eyes fixed on his supposed prey, a violent almost cruel snarl on his lips.

It was on these occasions that most of us saw Chouchou for what he was – a dangerous and wild animal, at least under the surface! And this was in spite of the fact that he spent most of his time around people, his head enjoying a friendly pat, his tail wagging at any sign of affection.

I remember Mum saying once: "You know, I've seen him overtake and run down a small goat! Saw it with my own two eyes I did... He chased the creature round and round before finally pouncing on it and wrestling it to the ground. His feet never stopped pumping, but his maw never dug into the animal. In fact, the little thing twisted out from under him and skittered away... Chouchou let it too... It was the damndest thing."

It was a small goat, I remember thinking when I listened to her go on – not the most physically imposing of animals... It probably couldn't run all that fast either. But in Chouchou's defence, I think he was only about four or five months old when this had happened, still more a pup than anything else.

Despite his name, which meant ugly twice over, Chouchou wasn't an unattractive dog. His fur was thick and soft to the touch, and his eyes were clear – you could say sparkling. As he grew and got bigger, we realised he was a tobet, a Kazakh sheepdog known for its size and reliability. At four, perhaps five, months – we weren't really sure of his age – he was already sturdy and strong, possessing the strength and power of dogs much older.

Wherever Mum went, she was always sure to call Chouchou along with her. One person, one dog, moving off towards the horizon together, drifting further and further into the broad grassland steppe, growing smaller and smaller as they disappeared out of view... I remember seeing that scene often.

It was always an adventure with the two of them, too, for Mum would stop periodically and shout out to Chouchou: "Are there any sheep about?"

In response, Chouchou would tense, and his muscles would grow taut; he'd take a step or two and scan the skyline intensely. I should say Chouchou understood not only the word for gazelle but also the word for sheep.

Saihu was much older than Chouchou, and she understood a far greater number of human words. Rabbit, chicken, duck – words like these.

"Are there any rabbits about?" That was all anyone needed to ask, and she would take off running, her lumbering buttocks jostling back and forth, scanning the area for any bounding long-eared rodent. "How about any ducks?" Her head would cock in the direction of the water. "Chickens?" And she'd chase after them until she was told to stop.

We raised a great number of dogs. But out of all of them, Chouchou was perhaps the least ugly, in spite of his name. Another dog we had was called Benben, which meant stupid, even though he wasn't. Daidai meant foolish, and yet he could hardly have been considered that. I guess we had a way with names... which perhaps goes some way to explaining why Mum regretted the name Saihu and its suggestion of a dog that possessed the temperament and strength of a tiger...

I really don't remember where the name came from. Was it for luck? Who's to say, but she certainly didn't possess the courage of a tiger, nor even a cat for that matter.

Saihu was a small dog. She was gentle, timid – cowardly some might say – but on occasion she did take advantage of her one skill that other dogs lacked, or at least had to a lesser degree, and that was her ability to understand language – her greatest skill. She was a filthy little thing, although that was mostly due to the fact that her fur was white and the countryside could be unforgiving in these matters. But she did have an ear for words.

She never wandered very far, either. Whereas Chouchou's territory encompassed the barren wasteland that stretched to the horizon, including the sunflower fields, Saihu's domain centred on our yurt and reached only a hundred metres or so beyond it. Her much smaller territory meant she'd never actually seen a gazelle, but that wouldn't stop her from displaying acute rage whenever she heard the men and women speak this intruder's name.

Her rage notwithstanding, Saihu was never once brought along to the great hunt the men launched each year. Chouchou, on the other hand, was a regular and eager participant. In truth, the men wanted him to join them in battle because his strength and keen senses were an advantage in the hunt for gazelles. Indeed, the mere mention of the hunt would prick his ears, and a moment later he'd be at the door, howling into the distance. I guess he understood that word – 'hunt' – too. I have to add that his howl was even fiercer than he was, and while the men would ultimately tire during their pursuit of gazelles, Chouchou never did.

I recall it was midsummer when the gazelles did disappear, an entire herd. The quietness left by their departure echoed across the plains, even affecting Chouchou, who seemed to realise his mortal enemy had gone. Mind you, it didn't stop him from staring hard at every shadow that skirted across the horizon, ever alert, ever ready. Nor did it affect him on the walks he took with Mum, for each time she asked him if there were sheep nearby, he would quickly grow stiff and primed, ready to jump into action. But their vanishing act hung on everyone.

Chouchou was no longer a little pup by this time. He'd grown big and strong, tall and muscular, mighty and brave – a truly impressive sight.

As for Saihu, her interests had shifted to an enemy much more her size. She'd discovered field mice, or at least their underground burrows, and so would spend her days chasing down the tiresome rodents – not beyond her hundred-metre radius, of course, but within it she tore through every single burrow, digging furiously with her paws until they dripped with blood. And even then she wouldn't stop.

Why?

Well, that's the real shame of it. Poor Saihu was woefully under-fed, for all Mum could spare her were meagre scraps and not much else.

3

OUR YURT

The two dogs went everywhere with Mum, even enjoying her predominantly vegetarian meals taken alongside the sunflower fields. Chouchou loved the Indian lettuce Mum always brought with her. For Saihu, it was the carrots. And together they enjoyed the chicken feed, as well as chasing the fowl about. Indeed, it was a constant chaotic carnival of fluttering feathers and half attempts to fly, of dogs leaping and nipping at their wings – a great commotion!

But... was the chicken feed any good? After all, it was only coarse bits of wheat and bran mixed with cornmeal... and then a measure of water to congeal it together...

Living out in the wilderness meant one's meals were simple. They had to be. You also had to put up with a lot – with everything – even if you didn't really want to. Ironically, out of all of the families who lived near these ten thousand acres of sunflower fields, my family had the most difficult time putting up with things.

When the time came to plough the fields and till the land, the mere thought of having to travel more than a hundred kilometres away from the village, the inconvenience of the whole endeavour, Mum's unwillingness to trust anyone to look after our home, all meant we packed everything up, our yurt included, and relocated out into the wilderness.

Even the chickens, the rabbits, Chouchou and Saihu – that's why we were out here in the first place.

We'd always try and re-pitch our yurt closest to one of the canals that were used to irrigate the fields, which was quite deliberate on my mum's part as it would allow her the opportunity to add to her menagerie: some additional ducks, perhaps a few more geese.

Unfortunately, on this most recent occasion, Mum miscalculated, for the canal she'd chosen hadn't seen water in nearly eight hundred years. As a result, our ducks and geese spent the summer mired in dust and dirt, ultimately losing the sheen off their feathers – their dignity, too.

Ultimately, we had little choice but to relocate, finally pitching the yurt on open land nearest the sunflower fields. Chouchou would sleep outside, Saihu inside. Of course, the slightest sound off in the wilderness would set Chouchou to barking madly, and Saihu would do the same inside the yurt as though offering support to her larger canine companion. Either that or she was egging the much bigger Chouchou on. During these times, it seemed as though, given the racket, we were looking after twenty or more dogs.

If something unusual did in fact happen, Chouchou would undoubtedly be the first to risk his life in our defence, whereas Saihu would no doubt cower inside and bark from a safer distance. Only after Chouchou had dealt with whatever it might've been outside would Saihu venture beyond the yurt, with her mock fierceness, to see what was going on.

These so-called 'events' generally meant Chouchou had spied some gazelles nearby. That or some visitor had come calling. Of course, the only visitors would be those other farmers out working the fields nearest to where we were, and normally they came to discuss the usage of water to irrigate the fields, or matters related to when we had to pollinate the crops and the collective use of bees to see that this happened as planned. On occasion, they would come because they'd discovered a new blight affecting the sunflower fields and thus there would be need for greater vigilance against its spread.

Or the visitor might come to borrow some tools. It was somewhat taken for granted that out of all of the households tending the land, we were the ones who had the most complete set of farm tools. If they wanted a saw, we had one. An axe... of course. We had a tool, or tools, to deal with any unforeseen occurrence. Besides the tools, we had plenty of other items, too. A basin... check... A jar, a pot, a table, a stool... check... We even had a number of potter plants...

Why had Mum brought along these plants, you may ask? Simple, she would tell us, they were soon to bloom and that meant they were useful. As for other families, they rarely brought anything with them out into the fields, beyond the essentials, and were more than ready to pack up and leave if things went south. But not Mum. She was always... prepared. Which also meant most visitors couldn't help but click their tongues when they strolled up to our yurt and looked around at everything we had with us. Our home was self-sufficient, like a little enclosed fortress.

"Shit, I reckon you'd be able to stay out here for a good couple of years for sure!" was a common refrain we heard.

We even had people come to offer to buy our chickens, but Mum would never agree. They were much too important, after all, and she couldn't bear to sell them.

"Then why raise them in the first place?" many would ask.

This was a hard question for Mum to answer. In fact, she couldn't. Instead, she'd mumble under her breath and prevaricate, answering by saying nothing comprehensible. Now, I must say it wasn't exactly like we were inundated with visitors, despite what it may seem like. At most, we'd have one a week. The rest of the time we were on our own.

A dozen or so households were responsible for tilling the ten thousand acres designated for the planting of sunflowers. Each family was directly in charge of their own allotment, which meant we were all pretty scattered far apart. With the exception of our yurt, everyone else had their lodgings dug partially into the ground, so they were more easily protected from the elements. They were also simpler to put together as they only needed a cover. In many ways they were like an underground nest, a sort of burrow, but for people.

Their choice also meant that if you looked out across the expanse of the steppe, before the sunflowers had bloomed at least, all you could see was the rolling land, the clear blue sky as its cover. It seemed... the land that is... as though it were wholly untouched, empty and clean. Our yurt was the only thing that interrupted the scene; the only thing that poked its way into the sky.

That is until the sunflowers began to sprout. As their stems pushed forcefully up from the earth, our yurt would begin to appear as though it were rolling across a lush, green sea, bouncing on the waves of new-grown life. Then, as the season progressed and the sunflowers began to bloom, there would be an explosion of yellow and gold, a great radiance that shone brilliantly under the blue sky. Our yurt would be swallowed by this new ocean of colour, no longer bouncing on a sea of green, but submerged beneath a sea of bullion.

The first year we came out here, however, we did like everyone else and built our lodgings under the ground. But Mum didn't like it; she felt it was too inconvenient, which was why she had invested a rather large amount – two thousand yuan! – on the yurt.

Eh... we had the smallest plot of land, we'd endured the greatest number of calamities, and yet here we were, heads held high. If nothing else, Mum was proud, regardless of the circumstances.

Our chicken coop – a wire-mesh-enclosed structure made of wood that stood half as high as a man – was placed as close as possible to our yurt. It was the second most important bit of carpentry we had, the yurt being the first. The rabbit pen came next, but it lacked the wire mesh and was made only with planks of wood. It was quite spacious, however, and certainly gave the rodents room to hop around.

The ducks and geese had no such quarters. Instead, Mum used some old pieces of worn-out furniture to enclose them, and they would, of their own accord, burrow into the ground to create small nests, or rather beds to pass the night. They didn't fear the cold as their duck down would keep them warm.

We'd be called awake in the morning by the sun as it crept up over the horizon and by the roosters that would crow their welcome to the new day. The echo of these crows would also call back those rabbits that had lost their bearings in the wilderness during the night. The ducks, too, would be stirred by the morning chorus and soon begin to cluck in unison with the roosters. And gradually our house would come awake, the morning smells would drift out of the yurt, and the pitter-patter of rabbit feet would grow ever more eager and impatient.

Mum greeted the day with a yawn or two, and then she would pull herself out of her slumber. She'd step outside and gaze first at the rabbits that seemed to be presenting themselves for morning roll call. Not one missing. Little reddish eyes would stare back at her, all the redder in the morning sun.

Why did the rabbits lose their way in the evenings? Mum always said it was because of their diminutive stature. They'd hop around throughout the night, and before long they wouldn't be able to see over the walled enclosure; thus, they wouldn't see our yurt. If we were talking about Saihu and something far off in the distance, well, she would simply stand up on her hind legs and see that much farther. She could do this for long periods of time, too. I just wished she'd actually stride off in the direction of whatever it was she saw instead of remaining where she stood. As for Chouchou, he couldn't stand on his hind legs. But he didn't really need to. He was, after all, a tobet – a strong, powerful breed that already stood tall above the ground while on four legs. And nothing could escape his piercing eyes.

The chickens were short as well, but they had never lost their way. During the day, they would roam, quite carefree, across the countryside, but as soon as the sun began to slant and creep beyond the skyline, its warm rays lessening, the chickens would all scurry back into their coop, unwilling, it seemed, to be out past dark. I don't think they necessarily remembered the path back, nor did they identify certain markers, I just think it was all by instinct, a sense of direction. I don't know really, but I can't say I ever saw them look this way and that when it was time for them to return – they just did.

As for the ducks, they tended to stick together, returning at the same time, or all wandering off. They always seemed to be making a fuss about something or other, too, constantly clucking and making a great hullabaloo wherever they went. It could really be quite a commotion at times, one duck squawking, another answering, a great cacophony of noise.

By dusk, nearly everyone was back, except, perhaps, for a few of the rabbits. For Mum, being back in the yurt simply meant the fieldwork was done, and now the housework would begin. First, she'd prepare the chicken feed and then walk it out to the coop. The chickens would surround her almost immediately, so used they were to this ritual, their clucking and chirping drowning out most other sounds. She'd then place the tray upon the ground and step carefully out of their enclosure, making sure to fasten the gate tight behind her. (Lu Xun, in his story 'My Old Home', spoke about a contraption called a dog-teaser. It was a box for chicken feed with only space enough for a hen to stick her head in to eat. The dogs, whatever ones might be about, could only look on furiously, prevented from stealing the food for the chickens. We had much the same thing, but I'd rather call it a Saihu teaser, as she was the only one that got upset at being unable to eat the chicken feed.)

Why did Mum raise chickens? I guess there was an answer after all. To her mind, as an old lady there wasn't much else she could do... and more importantly, it made her happy... What better reason did she need.

As if in response to Mum's generous care, the hens would lay more than enough eggs... a sign of gratitude for the kindness she'd shown, I suppose. And to pass that gratitude on, Mum would boil the eggs and prepare them into a feast for the dogs. Paying it further forward, Chouchou and Saihu would seem to take their work even more seriously after such a meal.

4

IRRIGATED LAND

Although we cared for two not-halfway-bad guard dogs, they weren't really needed for protecting our yurt. That is, well, the wilderness in which we lived was so remote and disconnected from everything else that you could say even ghosts would fear to tread across it, or at least thieves with unsavoury motives would rather search for easier targets. Besides – and maybe even more importantly – we didn't exactly have anything of particular value, certainly nothing to encourage a thief to break in and steal from us. Still, though, my granny refused to be at ease. If she had to walk but a few metres away, she'd be sure to bolt the door behind her.

The lock itself was large and heavy, altogether intimidating, especially considering the metallic patina it possessed. Ironic it was then that the doorframe on which the padlock hung was a rather old and much-worn bit of wire mesh.

When Mum locked the door, and just before she set off on her motorbike, she'd always make sure to call back to leave instructions. "Saihu, watch the house. Chouchou, look after the grounds. Chickens, lay eggs!" And then she'd speed off, kicking up dust behind her.

Confined to inside, Saihu would perk up nonetheless, stick his snout out the door, just a bit, and bark angrily at her departing figure.

Chouchou's excitement was indescribable for he chased frantically after Mum's motorcycle, jumping after it, yelping and howling as he did so for the better part of a kilometre, until Mum could bear it no more and cursed at him to return.

Mum's morning excursions were usually for water.

The canal where we'd set up the yurt at first contained, at best, a few days' worth of water to irrigate the fields. This meant she had to travel quite a distance to get more. And it wasn't even for good quality water. No, usually it was much more heavily laced with alkaline metals than the nearby trough, but sunflowers wouldn't grow without it, no matter the quality. Indeed, the only good thing was that she had her motorbike, which would make the journey at least a little easier... if not by much. The most challenging part of this morning routine was the ride back when she would be carrying two large plastic containers, each holding about twenty litres of water. I remember asking her about how much petrol she burned going back and forth, particularly on the way back with all the extra weight... I couldn't help but think it was terribly expensive water... but I never really expected an answer. What else could we do, after all? That said, Mum did figure it out, carefully working out the numbers before claiming confidently, a few days after I asked the question, that it actually wasn't all that expensive. "Certainly cheaper than spring water," she added, as I recall.

Water rich in alkaline minerals better than spring water? It was saltier, bitterer... forsaking water altogether would've been better, wouldn't it? Whatever the case, I never shared these thoughts with Mum. I chose not to burst her bubble.

As it stood, the water we did have, aside from its use in the fields and considering its value and rarity, was used for cooking and then for washing up. Then, once the dishes were clean, the remaining dishwater was mixed with the chicken feed to create slops. If there was any left over, it was for us to drink. And if there was still some after that, Mum would use it to wash her face.

As for dirty clothes, well, we kept it all collected together until there was just so much that the day had to be given over to washing it in the canal. Those days were always happy days, great days for washing.

How much dirty clothes did we actually have? To be frank, Mum didn't always... wear that much, if anything at all. Her explanation made sense, I suppose: "The days are dry and they're terribly hot. Even just a little bit of work causes me to break out in a sweat... clothes only make it worse!"

Take for instance when she went into the field to weed. She'd start her work, wielding her hoe as purposefully as she could, but after a few thrusts of the tool into the ground, she'd grow so hot that she simply had to remove one layer of clothing. And then, by the time she got halfway through the field, she'd have taken everything off... it was quite fortunate for her, for us, that the weather was warm and that the sunflowers had grown rather tall by then – clothed or not, no one would be able to see her.

But what if someone happened to come by...

Her response was quick. "Who else but us would be out here," she told me. And besides, all the other farmers were too busy tending to their own plots... they'd only come calling if there was something wrong... and even then, well, Saihu and Chouchou would let her know of their approach long before they actually drew close.

For most of the summer, she'd be out in the sunflower fields in nothing but her birthday suit, a hoe slung over her bare shoulder, her skin tanning a dark, rich brown colour, ultimately blurring the lines between the world of man and the world of nature.

The sun would dance through the petals of the ever taller sunflowers, the soil beneath would be dark and moist. So moist, in fact, it would seemingly be trying to suck her feet into its bosom, like the sea refusing to let a castaway escape its watery embrace...

The earth's most powerful force is not its quake, but rather its ability to be a home where myriad creatures could grow up... Mum would be there naked, nothing to hide, nothing to depend on, just her, as she was. At times, her head, as unprotected as the rest of her, would grow dizzy, and she'd be near to losing her way. But then, as she stood on the cusp of being swallowed by the earth, a branch would extend and awaken her from her stupor, gifting her a gorgeous flowering bud seemingly sent from heaven...

She'd stand and wait then. The bud in her hand still closed as though it were a young lady busy in her boudoir trying on one outfit after another in advance of some romantic rendezvous. A young woman unsure of what to wear, unable to make a decision... Then, at long last, Mum's naked form would call to it, reach it with a sincerity only possible *because* of her nakedness, a bearing of everything and all before nature.

This was how Mum spent her days, weeding and pruning, sprinkling fertiliser as needed, all with an incomparable patience, a devotion to the sunflowers that refused further explanation.

The days devoted to irrigating the fields were endless. Beginning at the sluice gates, the water would gurgle forth and surge through the canals that had been dredged for just this purpose. Then, akin to a series of dominoes falling one after the other, it would branch off down long and narrow gutters in quick succession, flowing out towards the individual plots.

Gradually, the water would slow. Mum would walk alongside it, matching its rhythm as it moved forward, clearing the gutters of excess fallen earth when necessary. At other times, she would add additional soil to guarantee the water flowed where it should, and when the long, narrow canals were full, she'd seal their entrances to ensure no water was wasted.

It was such a broad expanse of land; such a great number of long veins of water. And such was my mother's devotion that she took great care to make certain each sunflower drank its fill.

Deep under the ground, you could almost hear the roots expand and grow as they slurped the water, while on the surface they were a picture of calm. Mum would crane her head then and look in all four directions. Her eyes would fall on the open and wide sky, on the empty and still land. Mum completely naked.

There were only her plants and the road that stretched into the distance, unimpeded by the terrain. Doors were open to the landscape, welcoming its sublime beauty.

In the gleam of the day, it was a challenge for the water to make its way through the canals, but when night fell it was as though circumstances had changed. There, under a greenish glow emanating from the moon, the water would rush to its highest point. This was, I suppose you could say, the typical behaviour of water in these parts, what it was capable of doing. Its summit was the height of the sunflowers, drawn up into the stems to feed the growing buds.

It was also the last point of the water's journey.

For three days and three nights, the sunflowers would soak up what was their lifeblood, drinking thirstily until they were fully sated. Then, finally, from the deepest recesses of the flower, the beautiful blossom would stretch itself out, wearing its finest costume, a magnificent explosion of rich yellow and gold.

The curtain had lifted, the show was about to begin, and a new profound quiet would settle over the land.

Mum was the only person to see the spectacle, perched there in her nakedness, but for the wellies she wore.

Her feet were damp and wet, sealed inside her boots, but her body glistened in its bareness. No stranger saw her. She'd become the most formidable of all the plants in the area, and her shovel became her sceptre. Her entire being had been given over to the sunflower fields, and she was heralded as their queen; her body had become the land's glory and honour, its power and prestige.

Much, much later, when she told me this tale, I could feel and see the pride it brought to her face. I could understand how she'd given her body over to the land, engaged in her own form of photosynthesis, I guess. I could see how her entire life linked up through this process, the patience it required, the hope that grew from it.

5

WATER

Irrigating the fields had a similar atmosphere to celebrations for the New Year. It not only fed the sunflower fields but also allowed us to wash our clothes, and the dogs, too! Each and every pot we had, every basin, anything that could carry water, was filled to the brim. Luckily for us, we had quite a number of these containers, and they allowed us to save on fuel for the motorcycle because fewer trips were needed to fetch water.

The ducks enjoyed the time as well and spent most of it in the water, busily swimming about. I guess you could say we all became ducks of a sort.

As far as our eyes would take us, all we could see were white, billowing clouds in the sky, and ducks across the ground. And in between us and the sky, there was a glimmering golden streak of vibrant life.

Chouchou spent his days frolicking in the water, too. His great girth made him seem more hippopotamus than canine. He even played dead in the water, floating lifelessly, enjoying the weightlessness despite his size. Of course, this frightened Saihu terribly. Standing on the banks, she would bark in Chouchou's direction, in a way that was more hysterical than anything else. Then she'd spin her head around and howl for Mum. Mum, however, would react without much feeling, and certainly little apparent concern, despite Saihu never having barked like this before. I suppose she thought that if Chouchou were dead, well, there really wouldn't be anything to do about it. Ultimately, it was up to Saihu to do something herself, even if all she could muster was a pawing at the edges of the water, never daring to step in.

As the water worked its way through the canals, the weather seemed to warm as if in response. With the increased temperature, more of the water vaporised, moistening both banks alongside the canal. It wasn't long, therefore, before weeds began to push up through the soil.

But beyond the canals' immediate banks and the fields being fed by means of the canals, the remainder of the landscape remained desolate and harsh.

The chickens greatly enjoyed pecking at the fresh weeds, devouring them without rest. They looked rather comical doing so, akin to some leader strolling through a garden, hands clasped behind his back, head tilted towards the ground. I imagined the whole of the underbrush had been pried apart, opening onto an entire universe itself. The chickens were infatuated with the new growth, it seemed; their eyes darted this way and that as their beaks twisted and mulched each new sprout. On occasion, one or two would abruptly crane their heads upwards, lift one leg off of the earth and then stay still for what seemed like forever, dumbstruck for some unknown reason. They didn't appear to be looking at anything, nor were they concerned with their surroundings... At least, they couldn't tell anyone if they were.

The sky spread out above us, a great blue vastness that seemed to be without end. There was a wind too. It blew through the weeds, lifting the grasses into the air and bringing the chickens into plain sight. Chouchou and Saihu were quiet; they'd retired from their frolicking and were crouched down, sprawled out on the earth near the canals. The ducks were busy pruning themselves, welcoming fresh new feathers to replace the old.

In a landscape such as this, the vitality of life, of a nature that clung hard to this small stream of water, well, it lost nothing when compared with the bounty and magnificence of life that inhabited the great rivers and streams, the great lakes and oceans.

Only the rabbits seemed uninterested in the splendour of the scene around them. They'd awake in the mornings, scoff down their feed, and then follow closely behind Mum as she walked into the sunflower fields. When evening came, the rabbits would be nowhere to be seen. "Rabbits... look! The water's come!"

No ears, however, would prick at the sound of those words.

The water came from the upper reaches of the river where a reservoir had been constructed some time ago. A reservoir... that's what it was called, but it was more a glorified pool, more a largish sort of basin than a proper reservoir. It was about two kilometres south, further out into the wilderness. There was a dyke of sorts on one side... not put together all that well, and then a repurposed valve to control the water flow. To be honest, it was a bit haphazard – a rather crude makeshift structure at best.

But for people used to trekking across a seemingly endless steppe devoid of man-made constructs, the water that pooled in this reservoir was a sight to behold!

I'd been there myself. I'd walked and walked and then suddenly come upon it. There was so much water, at least to my eyes. And it was so still and quiet. I swear it felt as though I were looking at the edge of the world. There were no birds flying about, no vegetation growing in the vicinity... it just seemed to be a great void in the wilderness... a hole carved out of the world. There was only water: a great expanse that shone under the sun like a grand, ornate mirror stretching across the land, flat and reflecting the sky above. I felt as though I were standing on the rim of an abyss and it was staring back at me.

The water in the reservoir fed the ten thousand acres, so it was no exaggeration to say it also sustained the millions upon millions of lives that inhabited the land. I admit I'm painting a rather bucolic scene; the water, after all, wasn't there solely for the purpose of bringing life to our sunflowers, nor for Saihu, Chouchou, the ducks and chicks to enjoy. But it did nonetheless. It was complete as though it had been there forever unchanged.

The loneliness of the scene, however, didn't really compare to the awkward relationship that existed between us and our field of sunflowers. That's to say... well... for all of our hard, back-breaking work, in a moment it could all really be for nothing, a futile exercise to no avail when faced by the majesty of nature.

I remember I walked slowly around the basin, mesmerised by its reflective surface. On the far side, quite a distance away, stood a solitary white shack. If the reservoir really was the edge of the earth, then that white building must've been perched on its opposite end. Who might live in such a place? I longed to find the answer, but no matter how much time I spent traversing the edge of the basin, I could never reach the structure.

Once I left the sunflower fields, my dreams frequently took me back there, returning me to that great vastness of water. There would be white birds circling it for what seemed like an age. They'd come from the south. Other birds would be in amongst the reeds, quiet and still. But in my dreams, I never once encountered the inhabitants of that white shack.

When autumn arrived, our sunflowers were all we could've hoped for. They glistened in the sun, a deep rich gold colour. There was a boundless quality to them, and they almost seemed to be clamouring for attention. They tried, too, numerous times to wake me from my slumber, but never once succeeded.

ME

I had another dream... this one about a life lived on the land; I had my own plot and a sturdy house built upon it. To speak of it now, well, it wasn't a life much different from what Mum had... and yet... it wasn't wholly the same. It was, at least, a more stable life, less dependent on the vagaries of farming. It was a simpler life, too, and I lived there for longer.

The dream came and went. It was both with me and it wasn't. On more than one occasion I'd made up my mind – I was going to search for my own home in the village Mum was in. I even went so far as to draw up plans, my own blueprints, so to speak.

Later, when I found myself in the town, this dream... the plans... were still with me. Whenever I found myself racing back and forth carrying out mundane bits of work, whenever I felt overly anxious and tired, or when my body just wouldn't let me sleep, I'd close my eyes, wrap my arms around my pillow, and there, in the darkness, I'd continue formulating my grand schemes. I'd keep changing them too, thinking up different approaches, getting lost in minute details... And then, when I felt satisfied with what I'd thought up, a deep sleep would be my reward.

I've been to many different places, and I've called more places home than I can remember. I've slept in more than my fair share of different beds, too. But to me, this was always temporary. I guess it helps to explain why I've never been afraid of change, how I've never dreaded the way things do not remain the same. Life is just that: change, upheaval.

At one point in time, I lived the life my granny did. I had a small dog like Saihu. I had a stable job and a regular salary. I was busy, but things were peaceful and calm. At that time, my large parcel of earth and the house I had on it were undergoing constant change, endless refurbishments – a new brick here, a new tile there, again and again, over and over.

I've forever lacked a sense of tranquillity. My heart worries too much, and I'm always anxious about this or that. As a result, I've had to learn to console myself that it's only temporary – it won't last forever, your house will be finished one day, just keep on, bear it. But deep down I knew, I still know, I was leaving this place, and I would move farther and farther away.

When I was young, I lived on a military farm. Every house was identical, the same shape, the same layout, the same materials used to build them. The only difference was that in other households red bricks were used for the floor, whereas ours had no floor at all, other than the bare dirt. Ever since then, and this has stayed with me, I've always felt that the best possible flooring was red bricks.

As for what made the best surface for walls, well, it didn't matter what kind of wallpaper was used, or how the wall might be dressed up, no amount of silicon either... nothing could compare to ivory limestone and the white patina it would give to walls. This was the same for anyone who'd spent their youth looking at walls covered and held up by old newspapers and too much paste. Limestone walls and red brick floors – that was my dream home. Simple, I suppose. Perhaps, but that simple dream has not become my reality. I doubt it ever will.

Oh, and I'd need a small garden to grow vegetables. It could be just alongside one of the walls. Then, next to the garden, I'd want two trees. Finally, I'd have a chicken coop at the foot of the compound wall and a small flowerbed... somewhere nearby. But this too was only ever in my head.

Why would I want a home like this? Would it give me a life of relative ease?

No, that's not what was on my mind. That's not what I was thinking. No, in such a house I could easily wait for...

But it's not to be... all I feel at ease about is leaving, and setting out on the next long journey.

COMINGS AND GOINGS

I'm an expert at leaving, whereas Mum's the opposite.

Whenever she showed up, she always brought with her bad weather and far too much luggage. Her arrivals were akin to a blizzard sweeping down from the mountains. She'd be carrying a large bundle on her back, two more bags over her shoulders, and something else besides in each hand. If you didn't know better, you'd think the bags had abducted her and not that she was carrying them.

Indeed, she looked as though she was about to collapse under the strain, until she deftly released the ropes she'd tied around herself – these had been keeping everything in place – and let the bundles hit the ground. More surprising still was her composure. She wouldn't be gasping for air in spite of the weight she'd been carrying, nor was she intent on sitting down to relax a little. Instead, she quickly urged me to accompany her down the steps to get the rest of the things she'd brought. I was at a loss for words. She'd come as a tornado. What could I do but follow after her like some enraptured storm-chaser? And then, what did I see on the landing but twice as many things as she'd carried up to the front door. She was a true force of nature.

As for what was waiting for me, well, it seemed as though Mum had brought a little of everything, from knick-knacks to larger items; a whole slew of odds and ends. But out of it all, the most valuable items were the two baguette-shaped trunks.

To be precise, they were two pine trunks, both nearly perfectly straight and fairly slender, each tapering out on one end, the first similar to a tennis racket, the other more like a ping pong paddle. They were both about three metres long...

I thought to myself it must've been rather difficult for her to carry these on the bus, especially considering the regulations that prevent the drivers from loading luggage and other belongings on the roof. Would they've fit in the undercarriage compartment? I didn't think so. What about laying them down in the aisle inside the bus? They wouldn't have allowed that for sure. Besides, she had to take three different buses just to get here, so how'd she do it? A mystery, that's what it was... and she was determined to leave it at that.

Once inside my place, the trunks from the pine trees were laid on my balcony. Afterwards... I was told to use them for drying clothes...

"Look! They don't take up too much space, do they? They're just the right height, too. Aren't they great... long, slender... and oh so straight! Do you know how long I looked for them... to find that quality? I tell you... they weren't easy to find... perfect! Absolutely perfect!"

She'd brought them all the way to Altay, where I was then living.

It's true. She'd carried these three-metre-long chunks of wood, as well as the rest of her luggage, all the way to Altay, a remote provincial town in the far northern reaches of Xinjiang. She had to take those three different buses, switching three times in stations that weren't really stations at all; I mean, there wouldn't've been any waiting rooms to sit down in, or braziers to fend off the winter cold. She'd've travelled on provincial highways and across national motorways, waited at intersections between the two for the next bus; there'd have been no villages on the way either, no shops to pick up a snack or a drink. And during that whole time she'd've had to have watched all that luggage... in the wind and the snow. There wouldn't've been any bus schedule to look at either, if even the buses ran on time. She told me later that on the very first day she'd set off, she'd had to wait half a day before the bus arrived. She'd been cold and hungry, but she'd waited. Finally, an old man, another villager, had happened by and told her the bus had broken down and that there'd be no service for at least a day... that didn't stop her, however, from waiting in the same spot the following morning, hoping beyond hope the bus would come.

It's that last glimmer of hope that's the strongest, isn't it? The hope that visits us when things couldn't be bleaker...

The bus did ultimately arrive. In the wailing wind and snow, on an empty landscape that seemed to stretch on into nothingness, the driver had finally crested the horizon in the direction of where she waited. To his eyes, he'd seen only shapes in the blizzard... some... cluster of things at the intersection... and a darkish form standing out in stark contrast to the white blanket of snow. He thought it must've been a good three or five people standing at the stop. He'd seen that before, even in conditions like these. But when he slowed the bus and brought it to a halt, he realised it was but one person... and about three to five pieces of luggage.

It was in spite of such... challenges... that she'd brought me the two wooden trunks.

They were long, straight, and about equal in size, and without a doubt incredibly rare. But they were really quite delicate. My mum thought they were of course perfect for a city girl. It never occurred to her that I had more... modern ways of drying clothes.

When I moved house sometime later, I didn't even bring them with me. I had no way to move the pine trunks in any case, so I left them for the landlord to do with as he wished. I can't say why, but I didn't even think they were a loss. Giving them up didn't really register with me.

I ended up moving quite a bit over the years, before finally quitting my job.

"If you end up leaving Altay, be sure you bring the pine trunks with you..." Mum had told me this not long after she'd learned of me leaving my job. It was the first time I'd felt a pang of guilt at having already left them so long ago... Until then, I hadn't even thought about them.

I thought it best to tell her, and I remember hearing the profound hurt in her voice, too. They were of such high quality, their shape, length and delicateness... They were absolutely perfect... "How could you have just... just thrown them away!" she yelled. She'd made no mention of how difficult it'd been bringing them all the way to Altay...

This was sometime around the year 2003 I think. I'd been working in the town for a couple of years... and failing miserably at taking care of myself and my granny. My salary was six hundred yuan a month. Two hundred went to rent, two hundred went to heating our apartment, and the last two hundred was for living costs. Needless to say, things were tight.

The first time my mum visited me in Altay, she wasted no time in swapping out the thirty watt bulbs I had in the apartment and replacing them with fifteen watt ones. The second thing she did was help me hunt down and eradicate the cockroaches that were sharing the apartment with us. At the time, I was loath to kill anything that was living. The consequences of her visit brought calamity and upheaval, even though she never really stayed for long.

Her first order of business was the cockroaches. Her strategy for dealing with them was... unique... and involved a boiling pot of water. How, you might wonder, would this deal with our cockroach infestation? Well, the pot was first filled to the brim and then placed atop the radiator in order for it to boil. Once it reached the appropriate temperature, a great torrent of scalding water exploded like a bomb going off, drenching the floor and causing the cockroaches to scatter everywhere. Their escape, however, was only in vain as the water had done its damage, and soon we were left with a soaked floor and bug carcasses splayed everywhere. Satisfied her assault had had the intended effect, Mum turned her attention to other matters: shopping.

It was rare for someone from the countryside to visit the city, so it wasn't surprising she had a long list of items she wanted.

However, it wasn't long before she began to feel most of the stuff on her list was far too expensive, so she ended up buying only a few vegetables and not much else.

I suppose you could say fresh produce can be bought anywhere, but the vegetables in Altay were much cheaper than in Koktokay County, and Mum was even able to buy a few potted plants that were just sprouting... These would come in handy later on when the next planting season arrived.

The weather was cold... freezing. Naturally, this made Mum worry about whether or not the sprouts would survive the journey home, so the only thing for her to do was to place them inside a thermos in order to keep them warm. Once inside, she sealed the bottle, confident the plants would survive.

Each time she visited, she stayed but a day. In that day, however, she completed as many errands as it would take another person ten days at least to do. When she left, it was as though an entire platoon had departed my apartment. She was always generous before her departure, always giving me at least one of her potted plants. Since I had no flower pots, however, Mum had to improvise. She found an old plastic oil container, cut off its neck, washed it clean, and then used it for the young plant. I don't know where she got the soil for it, but she did, and once the container was filled, she carefully sunk its roots into the earth and placed it on the windowsill. Because the plastic oil bottle was transparent, Mum worried the sun would shine too strongly and dry the soil inside, roots included. To prevent this from happening, she used one of my books to block as many rays as possible.

Once she left, the only evidence of her presence was the makeshift flower pot and the book she'd positioned behind it.

Unlike Mum, I was good at leaving. I always seemed to know what to do and how best to send someone off, or leave myself. I would help Mum with getting her tickets and loading her luggage. I'd even board the vehicle to make sure she found her seat. We wouldn't say anything. There wasn't really anything to say. We'd just look at each other and wait...

As we waited, my mind would be drawn to memories of the

past. Old hurts would rush back, hard and fast. There would be a weight on my chest, and I couldn't help but feel somewhat powerless. I wanted to... speak... to say... something... I wanted to know what she was feeling... desperate to know...

But in that moment, that stitch of time, everything would suddenly seem so strange and unfamiliar. I would feel a sense of awkwardness, embarrassment even, that I could never put my finger on.

I would also think... weren't we all but subject to the wear and tear of time... No... not time, leaving... The ways people left other people... that's what wore us down.

Then the bus would start, and it would be time to leave. I would have to get off... and quickly. Once back on the ground, I'd spin and position myself outside her window. We'd wave. And then that would be it. Another departure... another leaving... would be over.

The last part of the ceremony would be for my eyes to follow the bus as it carried her away. On this occasion, however, as with every other, this final moment would last for an interminable amount of time... a suspended sort of departure. The evening rush hour saw to that. And I hated it. Vehemently. The bus would be there, not very far away, unmoving, stuck amongst other vehicles. More than once I would long to walk over to it, to stand below her window and reach up on tiptoes to tap upon the glass, to make her notice me, to say goodbye once more.

But I never would.

8

FATE

I never once identified with the life my mother had chosen. At the same time, she never hid her doubts about mine. The only thing we were sure of was that there was no way for us to live together. Two months max was about the longest we could both endure. After that, there'd be problems.

But... when it came time to till the fields, for some reason or other it was easy for us to work together. I guess we both felt it was worth it.

In addition to her work in the fields, Mum had opened up a small grocery shop, a corner store selling odds and ends. She also provided tailoring services, despite the fact that out of the dozen or so households in the village, five or six were already engaged in the same craft. At the end of the first year, all she had to show for her work was an empty belly and no surplus cash. That's when it struck her that she was essentially trapped in the small town with little or no means of escape.

The autumn and winter were, by normal standards, all right. The shepherds had moved their flocks south over the course of the winter months, which meant they passed through Mum's town. And quite a few of them ended up lingering amongst its inhabitants, transforming the village, if only for a brief period of time, into a lively and happening place. To make things even better for the locals, the shepherds all had cash in hand – money to burn, really – since they'd all just sold their portions of cattle to be slaughtered. Mum's shop, therefore, did brisk business at this time. The only pity was that it wouldn't last.

By summer, the herds would be moved north again, and the village would empty. Mum would still open the shop – after all, what else could she do? But whole days would go by, and she'd not have a single customer. In the past, before her store, Mum always tagged along with the shepherds and their herds. Wherever they went, she would follow and set up her store where they settled. But she was much older now, and it was just too difficult for her to chase after the herds – too much trouble constantly setting up shop, taking it down, moving somewhere else, and then setting it up again. And while she appreciated the fact that she still had to tend to her fields, keeping the shop in town made things much less onerous and much less physically taxing. And besides, she preferred to refer to herself as a farmer rather than a shepherd or shopkeeper. After all, she had experience serving as a cadre and agricultural technician in the past, not to mention the fact that she'd been responsible for well over a hundred acres of land, far more than the ninety she had now.

As for me, I felt this was all so boring. Maintaining a shop, a farm... all I could do was to use... a literary sort of imagination... pretend it was all something more... That was the only way I could keep coming back to it.

The year Mum decided to sow the land was the year I quit work. I'd already been at it for five years, and by then I'd saved about five thousand yuan. I'd gained confidence from this and felt I'd experienced enough change in my life. I also thought it was time to return home and be with Mum, to till the soil with her... be the farmer she was.

But ultimately I chose to accompany the shepherds when they moved north in the summer. I wanted to experience the summer deep in the Altai Mountains, mostly because it set my imagination aflame even more than working in the fields... it's no wonder Mum ended up despising me... or at least the choice I made then...

When the next year came around, I left work and went south... to the cities that lay there. But each time I found myself strolling down a bustling street, I couldn't help but feel lonely and exhausted. It was as though I had a hundred acres or more strapped to my back. I don't know why I felt this way... perhaps I do... but whatever the case was, I knew there was no escaping it... I couldn't stay here...

By summer, I was home.

Over the course of those two years, our lives changed, even though Mum and I never really planned it that way. The land, however, never changed. Lush, fertile forests shouldn't be cut down and destroyed, nor should barren, dry earth be reclaimed and forcefully greened. The destinies of man and nature are completely different. Standing next to the sunflower fields, the awesomeness of this apparent opposition terrified me. I could feel, too, that my wandering would never cease, that I was fated to experience ever greater turmoil and upheaval in the future, although I couldn't really say what...

9

PROSPERITY

I often think about the first farmers who settled in this area hundreds of years ago; they must've had nowhere else to go; they'd reached a sort of... end. To the north was desert, a great, wide expanse of sand that trudged on, day and night, swallowing up everything in its path. Then, up on higher land, those first farmers would've suddenly seen, far off into the horizon, a river valley carpeted in shimmering greenery. They'd've fallen to the ground for sure, awed by nature, and weeping bitterly. Of course, they would've had seeds with them. For age upon age, these itinerant farmers carried seeds with them... they were the only things that could never be abandoned, no matter what. There would be live-stock, too, for sheep intestines could be used as soft pipes to water fields. When they came upon a new piece of land, rudimentary devices would be constructed with whatever was to hand to survey and examine the terrain. If satisfied, it would be marked as suitable for growing crops, and then plans for the construction of irrigation canals off from the nearest stream or water source would be drawn up.

During the first spring when the fields would need to be watered the most, life would very much centre on this activity, and the farmers would never venture very far from the rivers and the canals they'd made. On those occasions when the water didn't flow smoothly, usually because a shoal of fish had swum unwittingly into one of the smaller canals, shovels would be used to forcefully unblock the passageway so that the water could once again gush out into the fields. Of course, the fish wouldn't have understood that changes had been made to their home. Nor would they have known what was for farming. Up until then, they'd lived a carefree life, growing fat and free in untouched waters. As a result, it would often seem as though they were trying to outdo each other as they pushed themselves in through the man-made irrigation ditches, only to end up stranded on the newly ploughed land.

At this stage, the seedlings could only be considered weak and vulnerable, and so it seemed as though heaven and earth were quiet in response. Under the sun's hot gaze, the corpses of the stranded fish would shine and glimmer, their silvery scales reflecting the sunlight. From a distance, one couldn't help but be duped by the illusion that silver lay bare upon the ground.

In winter, the stream would freeze and the people would resort to drilling holes in the ice, then dropping long lengths of red rope down into the darkened depths. Without bait and without hooks, the fish would still bite hard on to the rope and then be hoisted up out of the water. Such was their unfamiliarity with the world of man that they were easily tricked.

The fish had tiny, sharp teeth, and even though they would be pulled from the water and firmly held in hand, they'd still keep chomping at the red rope, refusing to let it go. They'd almost seem enraged, or at least totally spellbound. But there was no denying it – their world had changed, and a new predator was amongst them.

In spring, swimming against the stream, the fish would lay their eggs. Once these hatched, the river would be alive with vigorous new life, especially in the shallower bits around the bends and curves of the water. Indeed, it would be as though the river were filled to overflowing with precious pearls and gemstones. A truly dazzling display. If one were to dip a bucket in to collect some water, fully half of it would be filled with tiny little fish.

The people would readily hoist them up out of the water, too, pulling up enormous catches to be dried in the sun and then fed to their livestock. Of course, this had the effect of making the animals smell distinctively fishy, and then, when they were slaughtered in the winter for food, the meat, too, would have an unmistakable fishy flavour. The world had certainly changed.

And as is often the case when man treads into previously untouched nature, the fish population began to decline in direct relation to the increase in people. More and more land was opened up, and all of it along the riverbanks.

In the beginning, the fish swallowed water as if it were their breast milk, and later they sucked the river as though it were fresh blood. Later still, the river's course was forcefully changed and redirected further into the wilderness. New land was to be opened up, and new fields were to be planted. Seeds were scattered, and a bumper harvest followed. By outward appearances, the land remained uncluttered, seemingly desolate. But losing the source of water ultimately meant the lower reaches of the river began to wither and dry up... at an astonishingly quick pace. A few years later, what had once been a freshwater lagoon teeming with life was transformed into a salty lake, barren and devoid of life. The fish were gone.

Many years later, we arrived in the area. We stood facing more than ten thousand acres of freshly cultivated land. It seemed unspoiled, never touched. Even the road was new, with parallel tyre tracks clearly and recently etched into the wilderness. The irrigation canals were new, the cement seemingly poured only recently, and there was not a blade of grass growing anywhere nearby. It all looked so new and man-made.

Only the river was old, decrepit, aged beyond its years, now only stretching a few kilometres in either direction. While the river had grown shallow and narrow, the riverbed had grown correspondingly wide and empty.

But the fish had returned. They had endured an endless number of complications and difficulties... loneliness, too. But they had retreated further into the depths of the river network, and there, concealed in the nether regions of the waterways, they had survived. In a manner of speaking, we had done the same thing – us farmers. We'd taken the land we were responsible for and filled it with sunflowers.

It's possible the land was unsuitable for our sort of agriculture, as there was no mistaking it had become much more barren, seemingly made worse by the sunflowers and their oily quality, which only increased the wear and tear on the soil. That said, if we were to compare the earnings made from the sunflowers with other crops that could grow in the region, well, there really was no comparison to make at all. In this, we were no different from the farmers who'd come to the area hundreds of years ago and who had first opened up the land: we'd plundered it just as they had, choosing not to be concerned with anything else but our own wellbeing.

I remember that first year it was all hands on deck. I even came home to help with all of the work that needed to be done. Mum had hired a large truck to make things easier, and practically everyone ended up out in the fields. Even our granny, who was well past ninety years old, lent a hand. The dogs were there, too, as were the chickens, ducks and geese, and not a single flower was dropped, let me tell you.

During those first evenings, there were often no stars in the sky, no moon, nothing but a blanket of clouds, but still we were out in the fields, working. Mum and my uncle were busy with their shovels, turning over the soil and ensuring the seeds were safely covered, and that the reddish pesticide was evenly distributed throughout. Off to the side, I followed them, shining the torch so that they could see. No words were exchanged. We just worked, tirelessly, endlessly, tensely. The light from my torch would hang in the air, almost motionless, illuminating the red particles of pesticide as they fluttered this way and that way before settling to the ground, drawing a sharp contrast with the darkness that enshrouded us. The following day, the pesticide would be turned over by shovels once more and further swallowed into the ground. You could say the pesticides were the Red Army, I suppose, charged with protecting the seedlings, a formation of crack troops standing tall and straight, ready for whatever enemy might dare to invade.

You could also say Mum and my uncle were the commanders who had mustered the troops, had called for the military review, something like that. In a way, they were the formation's patron saints, their shovels standing as substitutes for batons. The pesticides would do the trick, too, for any such rodents still scurrying about in the depths of winter would only ever tread around the reddish particles mixed up with the seeds – hungry, yes, but too afraid to sink their teeth into the morsel of food. Later on, red would symbolise both hunger and terror for these wild creatures. In that same moment, all Mum's her anxieties – my uncle's too – were wrapped up in that same redness.

As for Granny, she would refuse to go out into the darkness at night; instead, she would stand in the doorway and hurl expletives into it, at a loss as to what else to do. After all, her advanced age had made her rather feeble. It had also prevented her from living on her own. In a different light, all her pain, bitterness and anger were, in a manner of speaking, tied up with that same colour red.

At the same time, my own sorrow and exhaustion hung there, too. I was in the field, but I wasn't moving – all I did was hold the torch, feel its weight in my hand, watch as its meagre rays lit up small paths, small cracks, in the endless darkness that spread out around us, drawing in all manner of animals and creatures out of the wilderness like moths to the flame.

The farmers from hundreds of years ago came like this as well. They were there with us that night, too. It didn't seem to matter they'd been dead for ages; they were there, tilling the soil, planting seeds. They, too, had longed for the redness – that mysterious, mesmerising colour.

The disappeared fish returned as well. Swimming out of the darkness, they dived tail-to-tail into the reddish hue that illumined the area.

It was as though I could see the sunflowers flourish that night. They blossomed and filled my eyes with a shimmering, scarlet radiance that the black of night could not absorb. I was suspended by a single silk thread over a great abyss that enveloped the world, holding in my hand a small bowl of water.

Torch in my hand, I didn't dare move. Not even an inch.

In the entire world, the vessel I held in my hands, the rays of light it emanated, was the frailest, the weakest imaginable.

That first year, I stayed until the work was complete, but once the seeds had been sown, I left. It was a hard year, especially because of the lack of water. Under normal conditions, most families would be polite to each other and even, at times, cooperate to get the work done. But when it came time to irrigating the fields, the lack of sufficient water dissolved all semblance of goodwill towards your fellow farmer; shovels became not just tools, but weapons in the struggle to survive and make sure one's fields were properly watered.

By the time it was our family's turn to use the water, on most days it was already well into the night. Mum didn't dare to sleep then. Instead, she would constantly go over to the door and look out at the supply of water. She had to make sure it was still there, that it hadn't been cut off. Ultimately, the only way she could be certain was to camp out by the sluice gates and spend the night there.

Despite her vigilance, out of the two hundred acres we'd been given responsibility for, ninety of them were lost to drought. Then the locusts came, followed by blight, one after another, until finally there was not a single sunflower left in the entire ten thousand acres. The only surviving remnants were the brightly coloured bottles of pesticide.

Needless to say, this situation aggravated and worried my mother to no end. And it wasn't just the destruction of her crops, it was the impact it would have on our lives, on us making ends meet. She was also disturbed by their loss. She'd cared for these sunflowers when they were no more than seedlings, seen them grow first-hand, and now witnessed them being destroyed, wilted to nothingness. For thousands of years, for generation after generation, this was the greatest pain endured by farmers – the loss of one's crops and the hard work it had taken to cultivate them.

It wasn't until August, after the blight and the drought, when the last remaining sunflowers on the ninety acres bloomed vibrantly in the waning summer sun, that Mum could finally relax and breathe a little easier. But by that time, most of the other families had long since given up. There were only two or three other households left, including ours.

At the lower reaches of the river, there'd been another parcel of land that'd been tilled and seeded with crops. It hadn't fared well either, and the old boss who'd been tasked with looking after it – well over a thousand acres – had killed himself as a result. The story was he'd lost millions.

It wasn't until winter that I returned. I don't know why, not really, but the first question I asked Mum was how much she'd lost. Mum's response summed up her resolve.

"Fuck all of them and their ancestors. It's a good thing we're already poor. I only planted a wee bit, so I've only lost the same. And if we're lucky, those sunflowers that were tamped down into the ground will yield seeds next year, and we'll be even better! I won't be alone planting crops next year either, and I can't believe it'll be as bad as this one, isn't that right?"

In spite of the dire situation, Granny had been happy at the end of the summer. She said to me: "My word... those flowers were so beautiful after they bloomed! A brilliant flash of gold, like some holy place or other... Juan... ah... it's a shame you missed it!"

Saihu didn't offer an opinion. I guess she couldn't... not really. She just lay snuggled up around my granny's feet... seemingly unconcerned with the human world.

Throughout winter, while Akehala lay quiet and smothered under a blanket of clear white snow, my heart and mind were absorbed in red and gold matters. Finally, I walked out on my own and headed north towards the river. Like everywhere else, the snow had swallowed the landscape there as well. A flock of crows took flight as I wandered closer to the riverbanks. Cattle trod in single file across the only path through the snow, edging their way to where the ice had cracked, if but a little, so that they could drink from the water below. I followed them. That's when my mind drifted towards the fish and I stretched my neck to peer into the dark reaches of water that flowed underneath the heavy sheet of ice. I seemed to see small trembling movements in the void. Then I raised my head again and welcomed the new snow that was falling. I saw those who had come before me – hundreds of years ago. They too had faced the snow as I was now. Like Mum, I longed to console them, and like a daughter I longed to weep.

10

NINE DAYS

During that first year – on the first day I arrived in the fields, actually – I found myself drawing water from the canal to make dinner. The sluice gates at the upper reaches of the river had already been opened, and the water had flowed fast and hard down the stream, which meant there wasn't much more than a little trickle etching its way through the river basin. It was slow, shallow, and terribly muddy. I remember it took ages for me to even fill the pot halfway. I had intended to wait for the silt and dirt to settle first before using the meagre amount of water I'd pulled up from the stream, but my impatience got the better of me, and it wasn't long before I had dumped the rice into the pot.

The sun had already set, and we had been busy moving house throughout the day – so preoccupied, in fact, that no one had even thought about preparing the evening meal. I felt bad, mostly for Granny. When the rest of us got hungry, we could easily grab any bit of dried jerky or dried fruit, grains, whatever we had to hand, but Granny had long ago lost her teeth and was essentially reduced to eating gruel or porridge. To make matters worse, her stomach had long since rebelled, too, meaning she could only eat food that was scalding hot – certainly nothing cold. To top all of this off, there was very little I could do about her situation, which made me feel even worse – it was that pain that weighed on me when I went to get some water for the pot. It clung to my heart still while we were eating. And when we were finished, it remained, a hurt that spanned oh so many years. Granny died not long after, but that pain lingered for much, much longer. It was as though she'd died because of that last meal, that hectic, hurried, laborious evening... Her death had started then... It was as if she had set off on her last journey that night... the journey each of us will take in turn.

Yes... we're powerless to do anything about it, about life, death. The only power I possess is the one to conceal how cowardly I really am, how frightened I feel... My strength lies in not showing anyone else my true feelings... it's where I live... in between... people... never revealing who I really am, what I really think and feel.

We awoke not long after the sun had risen in the sky, and the first thing we did was pack up our stuff and load it into the truck. We were to be on the road again, travelling about a hundred kilometres to the next field. By the time we got there, it was already past noon. It took the rest of the afternoon to unload the vehicle, the sun dipping behind the horizon, accompanied by billowing clouds tinged crimson by the sunset. When the truck departed a few moments later, there was nothing left to obstruct our view of the landscape as it rolled out beneath us in all directions. It was as though my family and I had been picked up by the wind and then deposited here in this untouched space. Against it, we could only seem small and insignificant.

I gathered up some nearby stones to construct a rudimentary fire pit, and some dried grass, too, and then set the whole mess ablaze. The wind was blowing fiercely and lent a helping hand to the evening fire. It took only moments for the flames to reach into the darkening sky.

Uncle scouted the area trying to identify the most suitable place to set up our new home, such as it was. He'd heard from other farmers in the area that there was an abandoned pit not too far away, one that could easily be cleaned and tidied up, and then have a new roof constructed over it. (This was before Mum had purchased her yurt.)

Mum was busy organising the small mountain of stuff that had been unloaded from the truck – seeds, feed, coal, firewood, chicken coop, duck enclosure, bedding and quilts, beds, bowls and dozens of round logs... She was engrossed in her work, her head bowed and intent on inventorying everything.

I looked after the fire, adding more wood as needed, and endured the smoke as it attacked and stung my eyes. I turned my head and saw Granny and Saihu not too far away, surrounded by a pile of furniture and household goods, their eyes seemingly chasing after something in the chaos. In the sky above them, a single, gigantic cloud stood watch.

The earth was coarse and rough, but it was also flat and spread out all around us, cutting a clear, sharp line between the ground and the heavens above. Our poor old tattered house stuck out like a sore thumb on the landscape, rude and disrespectful to the sublime beauty of the place.

Once the meal was complete, I quickly gave Granny the first bowl. She'd been starving, she said, and paid no mind to the scorching temperature of the gruel. She simply plopped down onto the ground and lifted the bowl to her lips, slurping it down hungrily. There were no vegetables – just the rice porridge.

Mum didn't want to eat, or rather she couldn't be bothered to fill her stomach – she was too immersed in her work.

As the sun dipped further past the horizon, the sky was emblazoned in a goldish hue. The dusk seemed to last forever, as though nearly half a day were jammed into the evening hours before the sun finally scurried over the edge of the land.

Saihu stayed closed to Granny, a quiet and comforting companion.

We slept under cover of stars that night, warm under our bedding and quilts. On the following morning, neighbours appeared to lend us a hand in putting the final touches on the pit that would be our new home. The work went quickly, and once complete, our belongings were moved into it. By the third day, everything was done.

It was also on that day that Granny wished to go home. Her walking stick in hand, she toured the underground pit, then strode out onto level ground, looked in every direction, and began to cry. She was well past ninety and had spent most of her life wandering from place to place, miserable all the time, forced into starting over from scratch, again and again. It was really no surprise that she found it hard to accept yet once more the desolation and barrenness of the world around her.

She tapped her stick on the ground, and the dull thud echoed all around her, the unspoiled earth hard, unyielding. "Can anything grow here? Will this land welcome new seedlings and see to it that they prosper?" Her question spoke of the struggles ahead, even if she didn't know it at the time.

The geese and ducks, however, seemed unbothered by the constant moving around. They quickly found the nearest source of water, another irrigation ditch, and dipped their beaks into it. Despite the shallowness of the stream, they were still able to bathe themselves. (Unfortunately for them, on the journey here they'd been cooped up next to the coal and so were now much blackened by its filth.)

By the fourth day, the chickens were laying eggs.

At the same time, the two dogs, Saihu and Ahuang (another smaller one we had) discovered a rodent hole not too far from our new home. Needless to say, digging into it to search for field mice occupied them for days, bloodied paws be damned.

It was also on the fourth day that Granny accepted her situation and stopped complaining. Instead, she busied herself counting the chickens and ducks, calling out to the dogs and geese, all to make sure they hadn't gone missing. The area stretched for kilometres after all, and she was concerned they'd lose their way.

Mum, on the other hand, was still busy with putting the house in order and making plans for how to begin ploughing the earth. Together with a few of the other farmers, she'd hired a heavy-duty tractor to help with the preparation of the fields. This had begun work on the third day after our arrival, and so by the fourth it was complete and the soil was ready. We started planting the following day.

However, this kind of work needed manpower rather than machines. We also had to think about the lateness of the season and make sure we finished as quickly as we could. To help with this, Mum took her motorbike and raced off to the Forever Red Commune early one morning. It was about a dozen or so kilometres away, and when she returned she had twenty-plus stout men with her. I guess you could say she had marshalled the troops... again...

Unfortunately, once the men were out in the wide-open plains, once they saw the land stretch off into the distance without end, they seemed to lose most of their composure and become rather weak and feeble, altogether quite a let down from the image they'd projected when they'd first come. Their work was slow. Each had a bag of seeds to plant, but they'd take only a single step and then stop. They did keep at it, so I suppose there was that, but the further they walked, the more and more they became enfeebled and fearful, as though they suspected they might never be able to return... that the land would somehow devour them.

Still, *we* persevered, and by the sixth day, the long, hard work was finished. With the seeds planted, the soil could now close its eyes.

Over the course of these six days, there were times when I walked up from our sunken, temporary home to look upon the land. On those occasions, my eyes couldn't help but fall on the great expanse of earth left uncultivated, still seemingly so empty. It was then I would turn to Granny and speak her own words back to her: "Can anything grow here? Will this land welcome new seedlings and see to it that they prosper?"

After Mum finished her seventh day of work, she returned home, and, like some strange magician, pulled out from the breast of her coat a beautiful bunch of wildflowers.

Where had she got them? I wondered. I remember I cupped the wild bouquet in my hands and marched outside, scanning the landscape in all directions for any sign of where they might've come from. Wide-open emptiness stretched out before me. Dry and unwelcoming. And yet... in my palm I held moist, healthy, vigorous life. How? The answer was not forthcoming, so I returned inside, found an empty bottle of spring water, filled it once more and placed the flowers in it. They were the only source of colour in our tattered, underground home. Three days later and still the flowers endured. Their life hung on.

I took to strolling once the work had been finished. I'd walk and walk, losing track of time, caring little for how far I'd gone. But I never found flowers like those my mother had. It was as if she'd already picked every flower that had struggled and fought against this landscape.

On the ninth day, I left. I abandoned Mum, Granny, our little dogs, everything, to the wilderness. I'd abandoned summer itself. You could probably say that I still have... left them there... deserted... and that for these many years they've been there on that same patch of empty earth, toiling away, lonely and bitter... with nothing to show for it... with the sunflower seeds still buried deep in the ground, asleep, dormant and unwilling to wake up.

11

FOREVER RED COMMUNE

In the year after I left the sunflower fields, my first stop was Dure, a little town nestled in the southwest corner of Fuyun County, where I could catch a bus to the larger county capital. During the Cultural Revolution, Dure had changed its name to Forever Red Commune, but this had been changed back not long after those tumultuous years came to a close. For its residents, however, especially the older generation who had actually experienced those years first-hand, it was difficult to use any other name than Forever Red. And out here, should a small rural town be redesignated as a commune, the locals would invariably start calling each other cadres or comrades and referring to themselves by whatever work unit they were in. Restaurants became canteens, shops were retail units, and hotels were guest houses. Out here on the edge of the world, we were the advanced guard.

In this area, throughout the villages and into the shepherd fields, the jacket of choice was still in the 1950s military style popularised after the Revolution, similar to the one worn by Sun Yat-sen and then made famous by Chairman Mao. The jackets did have one distinct difference, however, and that was their outer breast pockets. For the former, they were more in the shape of a penholder, whereas the latter's were much more rectangular.

Although the commune was at the administrative level of a town, the area it actually administered was far, far greater, stretching across the northern sections of Altay, from the mountains to the forests to the rivers that crisscrossed the landscape, to the southern parts where the Gobi Desert knew no boundaries. From south to north, it was a region of at least four hundred kilometres or more.

That said, and in spite of the large administrative area, there was really only one rather short street that flourished and did well for itself.

I'd got a ride on the back of a neighbour's motorbike – that's how I'd escaped. We'd taken the motorway through the Gobi and then followed a smaller highway for a couple of hundred kilometres before arriving in Dure. It was on this last leg of the journey that I started to notice a small bit of greenery growing alongside the road. They were tiny sprouts pushing up through the dirt, a rare sight indeed out here.

The further we came, the stronger the trees looked, and the more of them there were. By the time we arrived in Dure, the road had transformed into an impressive boulevard with trees lined on both sides, shading the asphalt from direct sunlight. There were even more trees in the town itself.

I remembered that when I was young, Fuyun looked much the same: there were large, imposing trees everywhere, and the people's houses looked correspondingly smaller and much shorter. To my mind, trees are everything. Their majesty is unrivalled, whether out in the wilderness or amongst more developed, populated areas, and nothing can really compare to a tree's dignified presence. The only other things that stood out in the town were the few shop signs that hung above what were little more than family operations. On still smaller storefronts, names were painted on walls in large characters, as large as possible, and they couldn't really be called signs. Not really. I saw one little store calling itself the 'Little Prince Grocery', a canteen went by the name of 'Aiyi River', and there was a shop called the 'Happiness Department Store'.

Even the bus station was small – tiny even. It wasn't hard to guess there wouldn't be that many routes leaving from it. The ticket I bought looked as though it had come from about twenty-plus years ago, one of those old-style rolls that you would pull off by the serrated lines, ticket by ticket. The vendor actually wrote down the details by hand – time of departure, coach service, and other relevant bits of information. Once finished, she unrolled the paper some more and tore off my ticket. I couldn't help but feel in that moment, as she pulled the paper apart, that everything was about to disappear. I don't know why, but the feeling was hard to ignore. After she passed the ticket to me, I stared at it for what could only seem to others to be too long. Another wave of emotion washed over me then. I was on the verge of some new journey... to some... where...

Queued behind me was an old Kazakh man, his shirt worn and torn. After I stepped aside, the old man purchased his own ticket and then with great solemnity offered his thanks to the vendor. I double-checked my ticket, just to make sure the info was correct... and written legibly... and then I placed it inside my breast pocket for safekeeping.

The old man hobbled to the station's main door and then was gone before he'd taken but a few steps.

I waited in the lounge, if you could call it that, for what seemed like forever for the coach to arrive. During all that time, no one else came to buy a ticket. The lounge was tiny, with only two rows of seats. I wasn't all that surprised, considering how small the structure was. All of a sudden, childhood memories of Fuyun County rushed back into my mind. It was a sense of déjà vu... The lounge I was now in looked exactly the same as the one I'd been in as a child... Perhaps it was the same...

In winter those passengers at the bus station all crammed into a small, relatively insulated, and all too narrow room to wait for their coach. Some would just wait, others would be chatting, and some would only be concerned about getting as close as possible to the fire that warmed the room. The source of heat was a small iron-sheeted potbelly stove placed in the middle of the room. Two cylindrical chimneys snaked their way out of the stove and up towards the windows to vent the smoke created by the dirty coal that was being burned. Unsurprisingly, the window panes were covered in a thick film of dirty water and steam. There was no way to see out of them, nor any way for those outside to see in. From time to time, one of the station attendants would squeeze their way in to pile more coal into the stove. At those times, the crowd would part as if on cue, and all conversations would cease. Eyes would be transfixed on the attendant as they manoeuvred the metal stove hook to unlatch the furnace door. Then they'd use a pair of fire tongs to refuel the fire, which would jump and leap as the fresh chunks of coal were tossed in.

Besides me, there was a woman also waiting for the bus. Half an hour later, I pulled some biscuits from my bag and shared them with her. If the room I'd been in had been just a tad bigger, if there'd been something going on in the same room we waited in, then I could've calmly eaten the biscuits by myself. But the lounge was far too narrow and cramped, far too quiet, and I had little choice... we had little choice but to acknowledge each other's existence and share the snack I'd brought. After we finished about half of the biscuits, she pulled out an apple from her own bag and handed it to me. We started chatting after that.

I don't really know why, I don't know if I said something, but the conversation soon turned to her childhood. She told me about the best and most exciting places in the commune, about her graduation performance when she'd completed elementary school, about the raging battles between the kids from other villages, few though they were, about how her very beautiful older sister had died... I just listened... and the more I did, the more I became familiar with this place.

Unlike their compatriots who still herded sheep, the Kazakhs who took up farming all spoke Chinese. But for her, it was still a challenge to communicate, to get the words out. She spoke ever so slowly and in a roundabout fashion that sometimes said very little, but there was still nevertheless something serene about our conversation. Her stroll down memory lane, such as it was, initiated my own travel into childhood memories. Hers was strangely similar to mine, I noticed. We both fell silent then as thoughts, memories and feelings from the past washed over us.

I wondered how much bigger the Fuyun County of yesterday was compared with the 'commune' of today.

It was a peaceful little county town on the edge of the world. That's where I grew up – in a small village of only four streets that crossed over each other with a neat, deliberate intersection at the centre. It was a small hamlet bestowed with more trees than I had seen anywhere else. Each time I found myself strolling down one of the four main boulevards – although they really couldn't be called boulevards – that ran between the school and our home, my rucksack slung over my back, I always felt a wave of peacefulness, of quiet calmness, wash down over me from those magnificent trees that lined the street and stretched high into the sky. The treetops grew thick and tangled, creating a large canopy overhead, and I felt as though I were walking under a resplendent triforium in some holy place, the trees arched as the great religious architecture of the past had done. The world in front of me dipped deep into the past then, ancient and old, full of wonder and mystery that still to this day entangles my heart and leaves me bewildered.

Upon leaving the street, however, I would begin to feel the weight of my rucksack. I'd filled it to overflowing with dead leaves and myriad coloured stones. There was a sublime and perfect symmetry to how nature created its forms, its plants, its animals. An empty bottle of perfume, a cardboard box filled with vials of medicine. When I was small, I loved everything and picked up whatever I found. Growing up made me forget this love for the world around me. But sitting there with that girl brought these memories back... I wanted to tell her everything about myself... but time betrayed us... I suddenly realised that in that moment I couldn't usurp her – it was her time to talk about herself.

A moment later and it was time for her coach to depart. Ticket in hand, we said our goodbyes. My eyes followed her out through the door and onto the bus. She was the only person on it. As I sat on the bench alone, it was as though she had been the last person on this planet... and now she had gone.

I still had quite a bit of time before my own departure, so I left the lounge and decided to wander about the station area. I never ventured too far – just outside the main door – but I did see a mother hen and her chicks busy digging in the dirt. Under the nearby trees, a cow lay quiet and unmoving. Across the street, a youngish, somewhat dishevelled man stared at me. The backs of his shoes were down, and he had an absent look on his face. I returned his gaze for a moment, looking for any sign of mutual recognition, but there was none. I decided to follow the road, and a few steps later I realised I had left the station and its neighbouring buildings behind and there was no one around. Courtyard gates were wide open, but everything was quiet and still.

I continued to walk, not really expecting to see anything, but then, to my surprise, I came upon a young boy crouched down in front of his family home, busy fiddling with something on the ground. A broken bicycle lay not too far behind him, its tyres facing the sky, one missing its rubber tube. I drew closer and understood then what he was doing: the missing tube had burst and he was patching it. His practised hands worked skilfully.

I was startled, ever so slightly, by the scene. The boy, fingers so nimble, couldn't have been much more than ten years old. His tools were crude and rudimentary. A beer bottle cap served as a metal file, the teeth used to slice through a sticky rubber patch that could be affixed over the hole in his tyre. The cap, however, wasn't all that sharp, so the boy cut through the rubber more by friction than anything else, creating a jagged edge – I couldn't help but wonder if it would be any good. The boy persisted, however, finally placing the malformed patch over the hole and pressing it down firmly to make sure it stuck. As I looked closer, I saw that he was cannibalising an even older rubber tube. By the looks of it, it hadn't been the first time the old tyre had been cut to make repairs. Clearly, the boy had had to do this many, many times before; he'd had to mend his most loved possession – his bicycle.

As I continued to watch him, my sense of amazement at his skill diminished and ultimately disappeared. If I'd been in his shoes, I'd have done the same... I had done the same. I remembered spending days as a child watching the bicycle repairman at work. He was a master of his trade, and I had watched intently, studying his technique, learning every step in the process, every trick of the trade. I knew, too, what the boy would do next. He'd patch one hole, seal it tight with glue, and press on it to make sure the hole was no more. Then he would refill the tyre with air, wait for a bit, and plunge it into a basin of water to look for additional leaks. If everything was all right, he'd deflate the newly repaired tyre and place it back on the bicycle rim. Once in place, he'd carefully pull on the valve to make sure he could inflate the tyre once more... when he was ready. The penultimate step was to screw the tyre back onto the frame. When that was finished, he'd inflate it and be off again, racing this way and that way with no particular destination in mind.

But I couldn't wait to see this. It was time for me to leave. I turned around and returned to the coach station. It felt to me as though I'd stepped back into the past, if only for a moment, but now I had to depart. The rules of time would allow for nothing else. I had a long, slow journey ahead.

The coach shook and lurched as it headed away from this little oasis and into the wilderness. I gazed out the window as we rolled away, watching the Forever Red Commune slowly disappear into the unending horizon. Forever Red had truly vanished. All that remained was the town of Dure. The former commune had been swallowed up by the earth... by time.

The asphalt road was old and worn, pocked with holes big and small, and no more than broken gravel in some places. The bus swerved and weaved its way around these obstacles, throwing us onboard back and forth. It was slow going... very slow. None of the passengers spoke, including me. We were all lost to our thoughts in this place at the end of the world.

12

A TELEPHONE CALL

While Mum was in the south tending her sunflower fields, I was in the north with the herdsmen. There were more than two hundred kilometres between us. Even trying to telephone her was a challenge. Sometimes there'd be no signal where she was, while other times I'd have none. On those rare occasions when the service was good for both of us, her mobile battery would be dead or dying, and if not, mine would be. When the stars did align and we managed to connect, we'd generally have nothing to say.

That's not wholly true. But when we did talk, it never really went beyond the routine. She'd tell me about Granny, how she was doing, that Saihu rarely left her side, and then the conversation would inevitably turn to the difficulties she was facing with the fields. Finally, she'd ask how I was. I'd reply in the same way each time: "All right…" And then there'd be silence, heavy and oppressive. I imagine we both looked to the sky then, unable… unwilling to say anything further… the sound of our breathing echoing in each other's ear. The distance between us gave rise to a sense of strangeness… We were estranged from each other, I guess, not just by geography, but emotionally as well.

"There's still to be no rain, you know… just what is it with the weather these days?" That was the only kind of thing we spoke about...

At the beginning of May, a sand and dust storm swept through Altay. The storm was so large it even affected the northern foothills where I was. I couldn't help but be concerned about Mum, as well as the other farmers, down in the south,. As if on cue, my mobile service vanished, and I was unable to even try and call her. It wasn't until a number of days later that the herd was moved fairly close to one of the provincial highways and my phone came alive again – finally I had a signal. I hastily tried to ring her... but failed miserably. No one picked up, and the call went straight to voicemail.

A few days later, just before the flock was due to be moved again, I finally got in touch with her. But it wasn't me who'd called – she had dialled my number. Her voice sounded hollow, and there was a constant wheeze in the background... I knew she was outside in the wind... but at least I could hear her if I strained just a little.

"Ah my child... now... right now... I'm standing in the middle of... an enormous field... I've walked... so far... so very far... and I've just... arrived... what an... amazing plateau!" Her voice came and went as though she weren't really speaking at all but communicating via Morse code... something, something... break, break... She sounded exhausted... and yet determined to holler over the wind.

Even through the howl, however, I could tell she was proud of what she had found – immensely pleased. Her choice of words in describing the field made it plain as day. It was untouched land, she told me, a high plateau, the only one in the entire region, and farther away from home than she'd ever been. It's unique geography, she said, had concealed it from everyone; that is, everyone except her...

I remember asking: "What about the sandstorm... is everyone all right?"

Her mood lifted immediately, and she shouted into the receiver three times as loud as she had before: "That's right! Of course... that's why I called in the first place! Fuck it, hey, fuck it all! You're so bloody far away, we have to talk about that... It's just been so blasted hard to get a signal! I've been trying for two days! That's why I'm out here... I first started walking south, holding up my mobile to see if I'd get any service... That was two days ago... Yesterday I turned west... then today... I thought about it some more... You know, really thought about it, and then I decided there was no point going west, so I turned north instead. There're only fields in this direction, but there's also the river valley... and across from it is the Forever Red Commune..."

"But what about the bloody storm?" I knew my phone battery would soon be exhausted.

Mum's battery was fine. A few days ago she'd been in one of the villages that stood near the river, and she'd been able to charge her phone. As for me, well, despite the fact that I had a long-lasting battery, and that I turned it off quite frequently to conserve the power levels, I was out in the middle of absolutely nowhere, tracking sheep across the landscape, one certainly devoid of charging points! To make matters worse, we were in the midst of heading even higher up into the mountains, a place that couldn't be more cut off from the modern world. Thinking back on it now, that was probably the last time we spoke for the rest of the summer.

"That's right! The storm!" Her mind had come back to the subject at hand. "Aiya! It was terrifying! You don't know... the sky, the land, the horizon... everything was gone... We were separated from the world by this humungous yellow wall... the sand... You could barely see your hand in front of your face! It stretched so high up into the sky, too! I don't mind telling you this, but I thought it was the end... that we were done for... I thought we'd be buried... enveloped by the earth! I've never been more afraid in all my life! Fuck, fuck, fuck..."

The wind picked up violently again, disguising her voice and making it difficult to hear her clearly.

"Hello! Heeellllloooo!" I began walking in circles, hoping it would improve the signal. A dozen or so seconds later, the service improved and I could hear her again.

"The sunflowers have sprouted, you know... but with a storm like that, if I didn't do something they'd be ripped from the ground and devoured by it... I couldn't let that happen, so I buried them myself! I tell you... it was pitch-black even though it was daytime! We used our floor mats to stop up the door... but still sand got in... The wind was too strong... and so we all ended up coughing and coughing... Sand was everywhere... Fuck, fuck, fuck!"

She stopped of her own accord then, before shouting into the phone: "Hello? Heelllooo! Can you hear me? Have I lost the signal again!?"

"I can hear you..."

Worried, she yelled into the receiver again: "Do you hear me? Why's there no sound?"

"I *do* hear you."

"Can't you say something?"

"I CAN HEAR YOU!"

"Hello! Hello?" She kept on repeating the same words, louder and louder each time.

All I could do was give her a solitary answer, one she had no way to receive: "I can hear you... I'm here... Keep telling me your story..." It was a reply that came from the recesses of the universe, millions of light years away... a lonely answer from some creature lost in the abyss of space.

Then, as I was about to give up, the mobile service improved once again, and we could hear each other. "Aiya! I betcha you've never seen the sky the way it was during that storm! It would've scared you to death... Fuck... I tell you... it was really something!"

"Geez... can you stop cursing, Mum! What about after... once the storm blew itself out?"

"After... Shit! Whaddya you think, huh? The sprouts were all fine, that's what!"

"I was asking you about Granny, Uncle, your neighbours... you know... people... What about them?"

"They're all..." Gone. My battery was dead.

I was light years away again.

And what would my poor mother think? An old lady constantly abandoned by the telephone voice of her daughter... What would happen to her? The phone dead, she'd be flung into her own abyss as well. Resolute, she had climbed to the top of the wind to stand on the protruding belly of the earth, the highest plateau for hundreds of kilometres around, the only place she could get a mobile signal, but now she'd been cut off, left to holler against the wind with no one around to hear her.

The storm had ended a couple of days before, and the fear it had caused had dissipated along with it. But that didn't stop her heart from worrying. To make matters worse, there wasn't a soul around to say this to. She hadn't been busy for days, which is why she'd walked so far, all in search of mobile service. Then she'd finally found it, had even connected to her daughter, but we hadn't really talked... She hadn't said what was deep in her heart.

"Hello..." she repeated a few more times into the phone. She dialled the number again... and again... before she soon lost count. Dejected and disheartened, she finally pulled the device away from her ear and tilted her head towards the sky and then off over the rolling landscape, marvelling at the sight. Two halves, cut equally. The earth below, spreading out in all directions. The blue sky above, whole, complete, expansive.

"I don't know if there'll ever be rain again..." she said to no one in particular.

13

THE HOLE

We lived in a hole in the ground that first year, as most other families out in the fields did. But one year was enough for Mum, since she went out and invested in a yurt once the New Year rolled around. Finally, we had more of a... tent... to call home. I remember Uncle scolded her for wasting money, for wanting to live a supposedly easy life, to which Mum fired back that he didn't need to join us in the yurt. In fact, the argument was so fierce – it lasted for the better part of three days – that the two of them could never really work together again. And so, after a year of tilling the land together, they separated. It wasn't a divorce – they weren't married after all – they just decided that each would tend their own field, and neither would be responsible for the other. They made sure too there'd be a buffer zone between them, about a dozen kilometres or so. If they were out of sight, their reasoning went, they'd be less bothered by the conflict that had separated them in the first place.

Mum hated the hole in the ground we called home for that first year. "Dirt... everywhere you look. Friggin' dirt! A bit of wind, a breeze, and everything is covered in it. Our hair, eyebrows, faces – all bloody white with the stuff. You sit down to eat a meal, and the porridge is white, too, caked with friggin' dirt.

Then, when you swallow... the crunch of sand... unfuckinmistakable."

Granny reserved whatever opinion she had to herself and didn't say a word. Either that or her vision had blurred so much with age that she didn't really notice. In any case, most of her days were spent sleeping. When I stayed there for a couple of days, well, all I can remember is her in bed – that tiny army cot – stuck in the corner, asleep, snoring occasionally, her mouth hanging open. With all the dust and earth swirling about, I wondered if I oughtn't to try and find her a mask... something... to cover her mouth.

The hole... den... whatever you wish to call it, wasn't even ours to begin with. It had been dug the year before by another family of farmers. It was about a metre and a half deep and roughly ten square metres in total size. For what it was, I suppose you could say it was fairly neat and tidy. In truth, we didn't really understand why the hole had been abandoned in the first place. At least, it made sense to move in and consider that sometime later.

Initially, we had to repair and reinforce the walls that had somewhat fallen in on themselves. Once that was finished, the cover, or rather the roof, could be properly placed. This was easier said than done, however, since the hole that'd been dug was wider than the planks of wood we had brought, which meant none could reach across to the other side. Our solution was to raise several support beams in the middle of the hole and then use two planks together to span the width of it. What we called grasshopper nails, a sort of double-pronged nail more similar to a staple than anything else, were used to connect the planks together over the beam that propped them up. Once these were in place, further wooden supports were added along the central beams to make sure the roof wouldn't collapse. It wasn't an easy job, to say the least, but at last we had a roof over our heads.

For the final touch, Mum tore up a number of cardboard boxes and laid them across the surface of the roof. After they were in place, a plastic canopy was attached over it, and then earth was shovelled on top of it. This last step would ensure the roof would not fall victim to the great winds that would at times cross over the grasslands and the desert. That was the plan at least – keep the wind and rain out, and keep us dry. Unfortunately, it was a rather makeshift covering. Whenever the dogs, the chickens, the ducks, whatever, walked over it, little holes in the canopy soon formed and granules of earth toppled to the floor of our hole underneath. The wind, however, was stopped to an extent... Of course, this only made Mum complain all the more.

"Once we get into July, the weather'll grow hotter and hotter, and so too will the wind. Our little hole in the ground will become like a steamer basket for dumplings... with us in it. It'll be so scorching hot we won't dare to move. We won't be able to... we'll just splay out here on the earthen floor, our bodies drenched in sweat. Who said these... holes were warm in winter and cool in the summer? Huh, who? I tell you, if I were to see that man... I'd kill 'im!"

Uncle moulded steps out of the sloping path that led into the hole. Afterwards, he placed thin panels of cement on top of them to ensure they would last. I don't know where he got the concrete slabs – they looked as though they'd come from some construction site. But it didn't matter because the steps made it much easier for Granny to come and go, and that was what was important. When news spread that we had concrete steps leading into our hole – a luxury not seen in these parts – our neighbours began referring to our home as a five-star hotel.

But it wasn't a perfect... hole. The main drawback was that the chimney for the stove was obstructed, which meant each time we cooked, it wouldn't be long before smoke swirled around us and caused no small amount of coughing. Even poor Saihu fell victim to it.

Mum had constructed the stove herself, building it out of mud and bricks. But she was never entirely satisfied with it, either. In fact, she repeatedly reworked it, constantly removing stones and replacing them with new ones, all in the hope of... perfecting it somehow. Unfortunately for us, she never did. All because of the chimney... or so she said. Ultimately, this problem took her to

Dure, where she purchased a new, galvanised iron-plated flue. She'd hoped this would remedy the issue – sadly it never did.

The roof lacked a skylight, which meant the... hole... was always dark. Strangely enough, there was a sense of security that emerged out of the darkness. The outside world was far too bright, even at night. Indeed, the brightness meant the world stayed alive at all times. There was only our... pit. In this wide expanse devoid of boundaries, only our hands, outstretched, served to provide but slight cover.

In the early morning when camels would pass by, they'd often halt their stride, circle back to our... home... then crane their necks out of curiosity and peer down into the darkness, fascinated by the contrast it offered to the world above. The more they looked, the more they would edge further inside. If it weren't for the size of their torsos and legs, no doubt they'd try to step all the way in.

Saihu would be enraged by these attempted incursions, but there was little she could actually do except bark frantically... and without end.

When sand storms swept up from the Gobi and descended on our fields, our pit was akin to Noah's ark lost upon the flood, the only safe and quiet space – if dark – in the raging maelstrom. And in that darkness, we'd wait patiently for the storm to pass, buried, as it were, like seedlings waiting to sprout. Once the tempest passed, Mum would carefully pull down the felt cloth she'd placed across the entrance, and then we'd emerge out into what seemed to be new-found land.

Within a few days of the... hole... being completed, I left. Escaped would perhaps better describe my departure.

Two young Kazakhs happened by on the same day, circling around our home first, before calling out their appraisal of the structure. "Not bad... not bad at all... You got everything inside..."

The conversation continued with them telling me they were farmers as well, and that they were the ones who'd dug the hole in the first place.

"So what is it... you've come to fight over it now!" I probably could've reacted in a different way, but this was the first thing to pop into my mind.

"You ought to be careful... this place is rather close to the irrigation ditch."

I realised then they'd come to tell us about the location and its drawbacks rather than to try and claim it back. Apparently, during the previous year when the sluice gates had been opened further up the river's path, too much water had flowed by the area, and the land had become rather soaked. As a result, some of the water had leaked into their home... now ours. So much, in fact, that they awoke one morning almost knee-deep in water, their shoes floating level with their beds, one of the walls already collapsed, and the support beams for the roof showing signs of giving way. Indeed, they weren't far from being buried alive. That's why they left. They saw no other option but to pack everything up, abandon the hole, and dig a new one somewhere further away from the irrigation canals.

Needless to say, their story weighed heavily on my heart, and I knew I had to tell Mum.

But there was little we could do other than reinforce the structure as best we could. Planting season was nearly upon us, and we would be incredibly busy. There was simply no way we could move; it would delay too many other things far too much, and we couldn't let this happen. I relayed the info to Mum, and afterwards, when everyone else was around, she told them what I'd told her. The first thing my uncle did was step back outside to survey the land. He didn't say a word. Mum couldn't help but be worried, which in turn made the day's work even harder and more draining.

Her nervousness, however, ended up being only temporary. Or rather she couldn't think of anything to do about the potential problem. She held up her hands in despair and exclaimed that all we could do was wait for the sluice gates to open and then see what happened. After that, all she could think to do was lie down... and stew over the impending trouble.

As it happened, the drought that year saved our pit from drowning. In fact, there was barely enough water to irrigate the land, let alone soak it.

Ironically perhaps, Mum and the rest of them would've preferred the pit to have flooded, its walls to have collapsed... that would've been better for the fields. At the same time, they were somewhat happy to have been spared this problem. Fighting for every last drop of water to irrigate their fields, to struggle so mightily just to survive, well, any other unforeseen, unknown problems didn't register.

Nevertheless, I couldn't help but be preoccupied by what could happen. In my dreams, I often saw the pit submerged... drowned. Granny was always asleep in my dreams, unaware of the rising water, her mouth agape. Her naked gums accentuated her profound weakness.

14

GRANNY'S WORLD

The year Mum started planting sunflower seeds was the year I quit my job. It was also when I decided to move Granny out to the countryside so that Mum could take care of her. Up till this point, she'd been living with me in Altay.

There was this one time Mum telephoned me. There was fear in her voice. "Juan... Ah my child, you'd better come home quick... Something's come up that..."

"Is it Granny?"

"Umm... yes... She's not doing well, and it's getting worse daily... If you see her now, I'm sure you'll be shocked. Heavens... her skin's growing darker by the day, she's skinnier than ever... I've never seen her like this... I can't help but think... she's not got much time left... Come home, please, and quick... I'm so frightened..."

I left for home immediately. It took two coaches to get there, I lost a full day in travel, and all the while my heart ached and burned.

Once I finally arrived and saw Granny's face, I understood what Mum had said over the phone. Her complexion was so dark that it couldn't help but terrify any onlooker. It was an unnatural darkness, too, more akin to the burned colour of a pot that'd spent too much time on the stove.

I drew closer to see her some more, then turned my head and spoke to Mum: "You've washed her face, haven't you?"

"Do you... do you know what... I don't think I have."

When Granny was staying with me, she was the picture of health, amiable and pleasant to be around. After she went to live with Mum, her own daughter, she changed completely. The bitterness of life had certainly bubbled to the surface. Still, could I blame Mum for this transformation? She and the rest of them were in the midst of... a great undertaking... I suppose... there were also the chickens, the dogs and the cows that had to be looked after. They had very little by way of spare time, certainly nowhere near enough to look after her as I had done.

When we were in Altay together, it was entirely different. I'd work during the day, yes, and Granny would be home alone, but I was always there in the evenings. And she knew this. She set her day to my schedule. As soon as I walked into our small neighbourhood, she'd be out on the balcony, her eyes directed towards the small alley that led to my apartment, waiting to catch sight of me, and then, as I drew closer, our eyes would meet and she'd wave to me excitedly. I was home. Afterwards, I even purchased a little dog for her, a female – I'm talking about faithful Saihu here – so that she wouldn't be all by herself during the day. She'd still be there on the balcony at the end of the day, waiting for my return, it's just that there would then be two sets of eyes looking in my direction – Granny's and Saihu's.

For me, Granny wasn't fated to die because of some illness, nor due to age. Death would visit her while she was waiting. I was sure of that.

As for weekends, if I didn't have any extra shifts, we'd spend the time together, usually strolling in the park, marvelling at the greenery, and other times at the supermarket or the shopping mall. I often wondered what Altay was for her... what it meant for her to be in the... city, such as it was. I remember each weekend before we went out she'd always ask me to help clean her up, to make her look presentable, not a hair out of place. She'd always hold my hand too as we walked. In her other hand would be her walking stick. We were never in a rush, either, but instead took our time... sometimes too much for me... just walking through the weekend crowds, her eyes darting this way and that, trying to soak up as much of it as possible.

The flowers that lined the pavement were especially alluring, and she would often call out loud, exclaiming about their beauty... on occasion, she even urged me to return in the evening to pilfer a few... At other times she would be drawn to the fortune tellers who were making unrealistic promises to seemingly easily duped customers. She wasn't tricked by their game, however. No, she was more insulted by what they were doing and would often lean in close to me to say it was all a scam. Of course, when she said they were cheating, her voice carried, whether she knew it or not, and was loud enough for bystanders to hear. Then she'd add that if we were quiet and didn't say anything, we could surreptitiously see how they actually tricked their unwitting customers...

In front of the city's aquarium, it was hard to get her to stop tapping on the glass with her cane and shouting excitedly that there were red fish, white fish, black fish... all manner of creatures swimming about... at least until the owner came out and requested, politely enough, that she not send him to ruin by breaking the glass. She understood what he was saying, even though it irritated her to some degree. After all, she told him, she wasn't some little girl or a country bumpkin fond of emotional outbursts.

The supermarket was where she got the greatest enjoyment. In that enormous sea of so many different products – compared with life out on the steppes – she couldn't help but fixate her eyes on each and every thing, looking them over as if she were some health inspector, and then turning to me to quietly offer her appraisal. "If the veg was a little bit fresher that'd be better, otherwise they're going to take a loss..."

Unsurprisingly, Saihu wasn't allowed in the supermarket. I had to always tie her up outside, near where the shopping trolleys were. She never appreciated this... She was a bit highly strung, it must be said, and would end up struggling mightily against the leash. Finally, we'd relent, worried as we were for her safety, and leave the market, making sure to untie her and take her with us. Then, Granny would make great effort to bow at her waist and smooth the top of her dog's head, urging her to listen and understand that we'd never abandon her. She would tell the little creature that she had to be patient for we'd never be gone too long... and we'd always return...

A month after getting the little dog, it was hard to separate them. Indeed, Saihu was always at her side, day and night. I guess you could say their lives became intimately entangled. They were always snuggled up to each other, and I suppose their lives became one in a way, sharing each other's air. It was really quite sweet.

But Saihu looked at me with completely different eyes. Indeed, when those round, rather beautiful, little pupils turned in my direction, I could see the lack of trust and confidence she had in me – it was as though she believed I was looking for any chance to be rid of her, despite this not being the case.

It was never the same afterwards when Granny and I went to the supermarket. There was now a level of anxiety that hadn't existed before... and all because of Saihu. Granny felt it most of all and would often mumble under her breath: "Saihu's just so sweet, so pretty. If she were taken from me... oh I'd die for sure..." I'd hear her and laugh to myself... Saihu was more of a mangy little beast than anything else – who'd want her but Granny? But at the same time, I'd begin to feel the same worry as her. Strange that...

After a day out and about, Granny would be absolutely exhausted, and once we got home she'd immediately collapse onto her small army cot without even taking off her overcoat. She'd struggle with the buttons as she tried to take off her coat lying down, complaining vociferously about how tired she was, and promising that that was the last time she was going to go out. By the following morning, however, her mood would've changed, and she'd look out the balcony window at the deep blue sky and say it'd been ages since we were last out for a stroll. On those days... I hated myself for not having more free time, for not having more money to take her out. All I could do was lie and say: "How about tomorrow? Let's go for a walk tomorrow..." I'd hold back the tears that wanted to fall down my cheeks.

Besides our weekend walks, Granny spent most of her time confused and not entirely sure of where she actually was. On quite a few mornings she'd wake and then start packing her suitcases, telling me she wanted to return home. On other occasions, she'd call on neighbours and ask them how she could get to the train station. She didn't realise there were no trains running from Altay, let alone that it would have a station. The only thing she did know, or believe, was that a train was her only hope. It was the most perfect symbol of departure she could imagine. In all her long life, it was only the train that had carried her farthest away, only the train that could now permit her to cast off life's difficulties and escape the painful place she was in. It was the only thing she could rely on... or so it seemed.

On weekdays, Granny's eyes would follow me from the balcony as I left for work. After I was out of sight, she'd step back into an empty apartment, and almost immediately her mind would fall on trains and travel. In these last years of her life, this was her passion. Then, when she invariably drifted off to sleep – she had little else to do – she'd dream of trains. Upon waking, she'd walk out onto the balcony again, waiting and watching for me to return from work.

She'd lost all concept of time by then. She also had no idea what fate had in store for her, not anymore.

She would also start taking advantage of my workdays to try and... escape? I don't know what to call it, but on more than one occasion she'd wait until I left and then quietly drag her luggage down the steps, intent on leaving... to where I don't know. She actually did this twice. The first time a neighbour brought her home. The second time I found her in a vegetable market. She was distraught, confused, completely out of sorts. When she saw me, however, I saw the anger rise up instantly. It was as though I had been the one who'd brought her here, and she was rightfully annoyed that I'd done so. While her face may have betrayed these feelings, she didn't get outwardly angry with me but instead prattled on to herself about her predicament. She was irate, yes, but I was saved from receiving her wrath directly.

Another time, I returned home to see an old rag tied around the doorknob to my apartment. I assumed, immediately, that the neighbourhood kids had been up to no good, playing at mischief, so I gave it little thought and just grabbed it and threw it away. The next day, however, another rag had been tied in the same manner. Later on, I found the same sort of cloth around the main door to the apartment building. Apparently, they were markers Granny had tied herself. Each time she surreptitiously sneaked out, she could never remember which building was mine, nor which apartment I lived in, hence the rags. In her mind, the buildings all looked the same, which only meant the city seemed like a labyrinth that she was hopelessly lost in. I suppose you could say they were her coping mechanism, a way to deal with the strangeness of Altay.

Needless to say, I was terribly annoyed with her. "You can't keep running off, Granny. What if you got lost? What then? What if you tripped and fell? Who'd help you?"

Granny wasn't always feeble. She used to be the opposite – hardy and tough – but after she fell about two years before she'd come to stay with me, she was never the same. Day by day, she seemed to get weaker and weaker. I remember I stood rather imposingly in front of her like I was scolding a child. I tore off the rag she'd tied around the doorknob, and then I confiscated her keys. She fired back curses in response, then started to wail plaintively, howling about wanting to return to Sichuan, threatening me that that was what she was going to do, that she'd abscond in the wee hours of the morning when the rest of the city, myself included, was asleep.

I was exhausted, weary, and filled with a certain despair at having to deal with her like this.

The following morning, as I left for work, I locked her inside. There was no way for her to get out, no matter how much she tried. She was left stranded with nothing but her tears, desperate and angry. Tears filled my eyes, too. I remember wiping them away and then resolving to myself that I had to make more money. I had to take Granny away from here. I had to rescue her from this life. I was twenty-five years old, and this was my most pressing, most urgent wish.

It was in that small rented apartment that Saihu first became a mother, giving birth to four little pups. Granny was overjoyed and doted on the little creatures to no end... at least for the first few days. Afterwards, the clouds of confusion descended again, and she was no longer sure about... anything. I remember clearly how her memory had failed her. We were about to sit down for dinner – it could only have been a few days after the arrival of the pups – and she paused before sitting, her bowl in her hand. Then she looked at me with a puzzled expression on her face and said: "Did Saihu really give birth to these little dogs? I thought you bought them... and that I'd complained about you buying so many..."

I didn't have the chance to explain before she moved on to some other topic and started talking about a family from eighty years ago, apparently with the surname Ge, and how they had used strips of bamboo to make baskets for catching wild bees, and then how they'd domesticated them. Later, when they went to harvest the honey, they'd get thirty jars at least, and even enough extra honey-combs to boil and make beeswax... Her story was detailed, specific and realistic, as though it was a genuine memory she was recalling. The hairs on the back of my neck couldn't help but tingle and stand up.

Before I could regain my composure, she'd shift topics again and start talking about her dream, presumably from the night before. She'd dreamed of someone criticising her, telling her she was no good. Her response had been to ask how and why, but the only reply from the stranger had been that she was bad through and through.

"Tell me, Granddaughter, is that true?"

I was somewhat flummoxed. In the morning before I'd left for work, she'd told me about this dream, only... the stranger had said the opposite. She'd still asked the same questions – how and why – and his response had been to say she was good through and through.

After some further indecision at our evening meal, I decided to remind her of what she had told me in the morning, and to get her to put the chopsticks down – she'd been standing by the table the whole time, lost in a sea of confused and mangled memories and feelings. That's when it dawned on me: I'd become so involved in her world, but there was really no one else on the same road she was taking. She'd already lost her way. And the only destination she was drawing close to was death – slowly, perhaps, but irrevocably. The only thing I knew was that I was... in a way... perhaps helping her through these... difficulties... through these last days, even though it wasn't my responsibility to fight with death over who gets to keep her. But at the same time, I was so far away. There was a gulf that stretched out between us, and it was only death that was drawing close. I couldn't escape the fact that even though I'd spent so much time living with her, days upon days, I was only ever on the fringes of her world, her time. I'd hovered around without really ever fully delving in. It was all so strange and terrifying. It was hard to imagine the sense of loneliness she must have felt... that I felt, too. She was like a silkworm wrapped up in its cocoon, separate from the world outside. Alone. Should I try and wake her from this slumber? Was it my place to disrupt and destroy her fantasy land? Or would that be akin to letting reality stomp on what was left of her... an act of selfish love?

Every day, when I came home from work and ascended the three flights of stairs to get to my apartment, Granny would be waiting at the landing to greet me. Always punctual, always there. It was the greatest welcome I could ever receive. I knew, too, that it was incredibly hard for her to do it. Not because of any physical ailment, but because it meant she had to drag herself out of her own little world, if just for a short spell, to welcome me back home at the end of my day. Saihu and I were the only two things she held on to in our supposed reality. And so I began to rely on her love more and more each day. I grew determined to hold on tight, to not let these few remaining moments of lucidity slip by. I couldn't just give her up. I had to do what I could to urge her to stay. I promised her in every way I could think of – she just couldn't die, I'd take her back to Sichuan, we'd ride a train, a car, an aeroplane, whatever means it took to get there, we'd eat its local sugarcane grown around Neijiang, we'd have *liangfen*, the cold jelly so commonly served by street vendors in Sichuan, we'd eat all the foods she'd longed for, we'd visit all her old acquaintances...

But it never happened... none of it.

The day Mum came to get Granny, I saw them off at the coach station. When I returned home to my now very empty, very quiet apartment, the first thing I noticed was the old rag tied to the door-knob. I cried then. A lot. Bitter, salty tears.

I couldn't escape it. I was a liar – one with great desires, but a liar nonetheless. And Granny, the victim of all my lies, stood there still, at the top of the steps, waiting for me. She was weak and frail, and so too were her dreams, her hopes. I'd done nothing for her, as useless as the walking stick she clung to in vain. And if I were honest with myself, I knew this already. I wasn't the one who could give her wings and let her fly. Only death had the power to do that.

15

GRANNY'S FUNERAL

The man presiding over Granny's funeral delivered her eulogy without feeling, without expression, wooden and hard. "Comrade Li Qin spent these last few years as though they were but a day... She was active... uh... energetic... She'd thrown herself into... eh... into the work of opening up the frontier... all in the name of... ah... the four modernisations... and uh... national unity... She'd done... um... made... ah... prominent contributions..."

I was standing in the assembled crowd growing more and more irate as he babbled on. I was also fighting against the urge to march up to him, grab the piece of paper he was reading from, and tear it to pieces. I wanted to attack him, to shout him down for the nonsense he was spewing... it was 2008 for goodness sake, and he was still talking about the four modernisations!

And who the hell was Comrade Li Qin? Granny had a name – it was Qin Yuzhen!

Throughout it all, Granny was lying quiet and still nearby, the casket open, offering no defence against the verbal acrobatics the man was gushing. Shit... even if she had been alive she probably wouldn't've said anything. She could be obstinate but also feeble. In life, she'd had only enough energy to keep on going. That was it. To have asked her for more would've been pointless. And now, well, that energy had been spent. She lay there unable to do anything else but accept this pitiful eulogy, this final indignity.

"... and we... uh... we must transform our sorrow into... ah... inspiration to work even harder than before... in our studies... our... um... labour... to further develop our... our mother country... and to uphold... stability in the frontier regions... Yes... that's important... That's how we can best remember... ah... Comrade Li Qin's... soul and spirit."

It was as though Granny's life had been erased and replaced with something she wouldn't've recognised... Even her death had become meaningless... She'd been superseded by Comrade Li Qin and her... heroic efforts... to develop the frontier.

Granny's name was Qin Yuzhen.

When I was little, it was Granny who took me to register for school. I remember the day clearly... She had to fill in our details, our family name, but... she didn't... She just looked at the receptionist and stated rather proudly that her name was Qin Yuzhen.

"What Yu is that? What Zhen?"

"Yuzhen, YUZHEN." Her voice grew prouder the more she spoke. "The *yu* is jade, of course, and the *zhen* is for something precious! Surely you should've realised that, hmm?"

In truth, Granny couldn't actually write her own name – she was, after all, illiterate. I remember I dropped the pen, then. Granny thought I'd done so on purpose and proceeded to hurl abuse at whoever was nearby. "So you're bullying me and my family name, huh! How the hell can you not know the characters for it? Who's trying to cheat me?"

At that moment, the image of Granny solidified in my mind. She was forever Qin Yuzhen. She would never grow old. Nor would she ever be beaten down.

That was until death called.

And after she had died, it was as though every last trace of her was wiped away. There was no connection between her and the man who presided over the funeral. He didn't care about her. Why should he? They were strangers to each other. Even the guests who'd come were strangers. I didn't know any of them, not a single person. Nor did Mum. If Granny were to sit up then and look around, she'd be just as amazed as us. It was her memorial, and no one but strangers had come (except for me and Mum). If you were to compare the faces of those in attendance, it would've been the three of us – Mum, me, and Granny – who were the outsiders.

Before they closed the casket, I went to caress her face once more. My heart was heavy, but at the same time I couldn't shake a certain feeling of… what I'm not sure… I had misgivings about the whole thing. The person in the coffin was so skinny, still and unmoving, seemingly resigned to the fact the casket lid was about to be closed on top of her. She was offering no resistance whatsoever. There was no struggle… How could this be my granny? It was so out of character…

After she was interred, a tombstone was placed next to the burial mound. Inscribed upon it was a long list of relatives – most of them had very little or nothing to do with Granny for the better part of her life. Mum's name wasn't there. Nor mine. Par for the course, I suppose, as nothing about the memorial service seemed to have any connection to the three of us.

When I was little, I mean really little, Granny was old, and I do mean really old. By all accounts, too, she'd already prepared herself for death. We were in Sichuan then, although I don't remember exactly where. Granny had, the story went, already sorted out where she was to be buried and what kind of tombstone she wanted. She'd saved up for a casket as well, which had been placed in her old home in the countryside, just waiting to be used. As I was little, I didn't really understand everything, but Granny seemed quite pleased… content… happy even… she was ready… all that remained was the wait.

But that wait ended up being a lot longer than she expected.

I remember how whenever she felt ill, especially if it was serious, or at least seemed to be, or when she just felt out of sorts, something not right, the first thing she would tell me was where her bankbook was hidden. Her last words, I guess. It was quite the hiding place, too. I don't think I would've found it on my own, no matter how hard I might've tried. Then, when death didn't come and she started to feel better, she'd straightaway find a new hiding place for it. Her vigilance in this matter was beyond reproach.

When I was a little older, she began to tell me how to deal with her affairs when the inevitable end came. I remember she taught me how to dress her in burial robes. I remember, too, her repeated injunction that she be placed on the ground, or on some other hard surface, when she was at death's door – under no conditions should she be allowed to die on a soft, comfortable bed because the effect that would have on her corpse would be just... unacceptable... or so she said. She told me, too, that after her spirit left her body, something – a pair of shoes, whatever – had to be put on her feet, and then some padding or other placed underneath it...

From the age of seven or eight, I began to prepare, to learn how to face her eventual death, to understand and deal with the pain and sorrow it would cause... and how to accept living on... alone in the remains of life. Afterwards, she accompanied us to Xinjiang. Before we left, I recall we lied to her, told her we'd be back in a couple of years. We thought she believed that in two years we'd be back in Sichuan, but she never really did. She'd worked it out by herself – she knew 'two years' didn't necessarily mean two *actual* years.

We knew she was afraid, fearful she would never return. We felt it, so did she, and so did pretty much everyone else. A Buddhist monk even arranged for Granny to have her photo taken as a way for them to remember her. They believed, too, that they were unlikely to ever see her again. There was pride, perhaps a touch of arrogance, in her voice when she told us this. *They* wanted to remember *her*. I figured the monk had meant they wanted some form of commemoration, not just a reminder... a souvenir... She was, after all, the oldest member of the Buddhist association. But I never said anything.

Then we were in Xinjiang. Days folded into months, months into years. And for Granny, there was no burial ground, no casket. These were all so far away in Sichuan. The gradual realisation of this increased her anxiety, and slowly, bit by bit, a feeling of nothingness, of disconnectedness, grew in her heart. At least, this was how she felt most of the time. On other occasions, it was clear she felt happy and free; she admitted as much herself.

"When I die," she once told me, "just lay my body out on the ground and burn it to ashes. Then let the wind take me. That's what the temple monk told me to do. We all believe in the Bodhisattva... and for those who don't, just ask the immortals, the spirits of the land to come..."

Of course, in a matter of days she would go back on these words: "Cremation isn't always what it's cracked up to be. I fear the pain of it... I'd be better off buried in the ground..."

Her burial clothes had been ready for more than twenty years. It didn't matter where she was or where she went, she always carried them with her. As a young child, I'd been introduced to them, so in a way I was as familiar and comfortable with them as I could be. They were like a childhood friend, I suppose. That's why I can't understand... when the time came... I couldn't use them.

Afterwards, when it came time to sift through all of Granny's old belongings, I soon discovered there wouldn't be that much to do as everything had already been neatly ordered and stacked. It was as though some clever kitty had got into the mess that was her life and put things straight. In a way, however, this neatness only further stripped away the bits of her actual life, the important stuff... the mess... that *was* her, not this...

Quite a few people at the memorial service described Granny's death as a happy deliverance. She was ninety-six when she died – a long and tiring life. It was, in a word, time. Or so most of the other mourners said. For me, this was not the case at all. There was nothing natural or normal about her death. It was evil. Wrong. Malicious, even. She'd endured so much pain in her life that it wasn't an exaggeration to say it was torture... and now that bitterness and hurt had been thrust upon me. Loneliness, fear, terror... it had seized her... choked the life out of her... and now it had wrapped its hands around me... At least, that's how it felt then.

People often said that when a person dies, it's like a lantern being snuffed out. But that didn't happen with Granny. Her light continued to glimmer, even after her death. Indeed, we could feel its glow in our heart of hearts. It illuminated our road ahead, you could say.

Memories of two years before rushed back into my mind. I remembered the first time we were separated, the moments before I left, Granny shifted her feet, her hand fell to the silver bracelet that'd always adorned her wrist, and then she pulled it off and handed it to me. But it was too small for me, so it made no sense to accept it. Tension rose up in the air between us. Another passenger pressed me to board the coach, only increasing Granny's worry and concern. I rushed a reply, told her we could speak of this more later – I would be back in the winter after all – but we both knew, we understood what wasn't said: that 'next time' could only ever be indeterminate, unknown to both of us, a vague and hazy concept. Granny persisted, fiddled more with the bracelet and tried to explain: "It's a 'memory'! The temple monk told me this. We all need... 'memories'... every time you look at this, it'll remind you of me..." Old Sichuanese had no such word for souvenir, which was what she was trying to say. I don't think she understood what he'd meant... but it didn't seem to matter – in that moment, her use of the word 'memories' had been... perfect.

She left the station still wearing the silver bracelet, carrying with her an extra burden of regret: she hadn't been able to convince me to accept her 'memory'. The only consolation, small though it was, was that she still possessed her prized piece of jewellery, the only thing she could still call her own, despite what it now might've symbolised.

And then there she was, quiet, still, stretched out in her casket, the bracelet clasped firmly about her cold, withered wrist. I walked over to the coffin, leaned over it, extended my hand and took hold of hers one last time. It felt like ice – hard and frozen. At the end of her life, the tender feelings she once had about giving me the bracelet as a... memento... had gone, erased like her life itself.

After the casket was laid in the ground, but before the earth had been piled on top, Mum and I left the service. We wanted nothing more than to be free, to escape from this far too awkward funeral for a person we didn't seem to know – this Comrade Li Qin.

I did, however, write a eulogy for Granny sometime later.

Qin Yuzhen, orphaned at birth, a poor waif adopted to serve in a wealthier home, finally married off to a gambling addict, mother of ten. Spent more than half her life a widow; saw eight children into their graves. No home to call her own, no *hukou* to claim residency, her life was lived between Sichuan and Xinjiang. At the age of seventy, under orders from the government, she returned to her adoptive mother's home, tasked with taking care of the old woman, a family member of a revolutionary martyr, by then a hundred years of age. Made a living out of collecting rubbish, raised her granddaughter on her own. On the death of her adoptive mother, the government evicted her from the low-rent, six-metre-square apartment she'd been living in. At the age of eighty-five, she returned to the countryside to till the land. At the age of eighty-eight, she accompanied her youngest daughter back to Xinjiang. She never saw her hometown again.

RETURN HOME

It was a return home, I suppose, for Granny's memorial service. First, I took the train to Urumqi, and then an overnight coach – more minibus than anything else – to the small town where she used to live. It wasn't Sichuan... not her hometown... but a home nonetheless. I had wanted to see her this one last time, even though I didn't stay long after the memorial service, or rather, Mum and I left before it was finished. We'd seen *her*... this comrade they spoke of was a stranger, after all. I remember the ride that took me to the Forever Red Commune, and as I heard that name... again... I knew I had left the outside world and travelled to somewhere else, a place forgotten by time. The bus ride was long, as usual, but that didn't stop another passenger from complaining for nearly the entire journey. Apparently, it was his first time in the area, and all he could keep saying was: "How's it so far?... Still farther to go?... How's it there're no trees lining the roads?... No... nothing?..." The longer the road stretched, the more panicky he became.

I wondered to myself how he ended up here, what fate had brought him to this forgotten land. No one thought to answer him because we were all so immersed in our own deep pits of silent introspection. No one except for the bus driver that is, who tried to console the man, perhaps more to just get him to shut up. "We're

halfway there... more than half... another hour and we'll be there...
you'll see trees and other stuff then... a river, too..."

The minibus tossed, bounced and swerved its way across the
highway, a road that straddled the Gobi, a great and ever-growing
sea of sand seemingly intent on devouring the world. I was too
exhausted to pay any attention. Still the man babbled on, the
tension in his voice noticeably increasing. "What made people
come out here in the first place? Why in hell would they want to?
What possessed them? How can anyone live out here?" The more
he spoke, the more he sounded like I did years ago when I first
arrived here.

I turned my head towards the window and used all of my
concentration to drown him out, to focus on the landscape as it
passed by. Although we were in the same boat, had had the same
thoughts, this was *his* first time.

Mum had been waiting for me for ages by the time the minibus
finally arrived. Her motorbike was leaning against a vegetable
store, the rear seat already loaded with stuff she'd bought.

"Want to go for a bit of a stroll?"

I looked east, then turned my neck and stared off to the west.
This was Forever Red Commune: one road, shops lined on both
sides. That was it. "Nah," I replied.

"Then let's get going. Saihu's home by himself after all."

I squeezed onto the motorbike, wedged between Mum and the
veg, grains and oil she'd purchased. Then, when the bike lurched
forward with a jolt, I found myself slammed violently into her back.
Mum didn't seem to notice, or didn't care, and it wasn't long before
we had left the small town behind us in the wilderness, an outpost
in the middle of nowhere.

If nothing else, the ride home gave Mum the chance to flaunt
her driving prowess. "Do you see those potholes ahead? There's
about a hand's space between them... That's it... keep your eye on
them. Look! Did you see that? Whew! We're past them right?...
Heh, heh... Do you know of any bike races in the area? No one can
match my speed and skill! I don't know if you see it or not, there in
front, those stones... Do you see them? There! That's skill!"

This was the first time I'd ever ridden on her motorcycle. It seemed rather new, actually, and I couldn't really remember seeing it the last time I was home. But then again, when was I last home? Come to think of it... where was home?

About ten kilometres after we left, Mum manoeuvred the bike off of the paved highway, such as it was, and onto a gravelly roadbed. A moment later, she turned off and headed down a small dirt path that stretched south into what appeared to be untamed land. After passing by a comparatively wide canal that flowed with very little water, we then arched up a fairly steep incline. We didn't get very far, however, before Mum brought the motorbike to a stop.

"The road's no good here... You'll have to get off and walk... There's a shortcut just over there."

Skills indeed, I thought.

Once I'd made my way to the top of the sloping hill, my eyes were filled with a vast emptiness. The Gobi stretched everywhere, its golden sand drawing a sharp contrast with the empty, blue sky above it. Then, when I turned around, I spied the river valley etched in the land below. The Ulungur was lonely and quiet, disappearing into the west. The trees on either side looked as frail as they were resolute in holding onto life in such stark conditions. The minibus passenger then popped into my mind. If he were standing here with me in this moment, overlooking this scene, he'd probably understand why the people had come...

The air was suffused with dust, an effect of such close proximity to the Gobi. However, a few kilometres in the distance, the only thing I could see were fields upon fields stretching out to fill the horizon. Their greenery was different from the stubborn vegetation that hung onto the riverbank. It seemed almost to float, just above the ground, about waist high. They were like some vast and dreamlike scene etched into the landscape.

I could see, too, that Mum's bike had traversed the only road... the only path... that could be seen. It'd snaked its way out of the green fields that had opened up like some great natural harbour before us. Then it narrowed as it wound its way through the landscape, finally disappearing off into the distance. There were several small forks, several small tributaries, but the path became no more than a foot wide before it was ultimately consumed by the earth. Standing above it as I was, it seemed to be nothing more than a lingering trace of some long-forgotten road. A leftover scar once cut into the firm, unyielding earth. I stood there, enthralled by the view.

Mum broke my reverie.

"This road's mine... It wasn't there before... Did you know that... Every day I went to fetch water... I still do it now... back and forth, back and forth... That's the shortcut I made... Now it's a road... see. It stretches on so far, doesn't it?... I'm the only one who uses it, too. That's why it's mine."

The road – Mum's road – such as it was, reached out into her sunflower fields, which now stood at least half the height of an average man, if not taller. As I stared at them, the wind dropped and left the air still and unmoving, if only fleetingly, and then, in that moment, staring at the fields, I couldn't escape the feeling I was looking at some old snapshot taken years and years ago in some other faraway place. As my eyes spanned the breadth of the fields, they finally fell on an empty patch of land. And there, on the edges, I saw the yurt.

"We're home."

Chouchou came bounding up the hill to greet us. He must've seen us coming from some distance away. Then, as he drew closer, he leaped towards the still moving bike as though he were going to embrace Mum in some giant tobet hug.

Mum reduced her speed. "You fool! What the devil are you doing? Are you trying to get yourself killed?"

It was the first time I'd seen Chouchou, and I could tell Mum was terribly proud of him.

"This is my dog... he's big, isn't he? Chouchou, this is your sister, Juan!"

The animal sniffed at my shoes, hesitated for what was only a few seconds, and then accepted me as part of the family. I heard Saihu bark... and then it was as though I'd been wakened from some deep slumber. The sounds, the voices... family... all of it, the memories, came rushing back. It was like a key had finally been found to open up a lock that had long been bolted. And with it open, the metal door was pushed ajar, just enough for Saihu to squeeze through. Emotions welled up inside me, coming in tandem with the open lock, and I nearly broke down and cried.

I knelt over and embraced Granny's old little dog. Then, when I looked up again, more memories flooded back. I saw the old bed, the mat that lay next to it, and the mottled old azure table, still as short as it'd always been. And the well-used greenish enamelled basin sitting on top of the table... everything... This was... home.

And then I remembered the previous times I'd come. They'd been like this, too. I'd come to some... strange and unfamiliar place... It'd been like this before... but if it wasn't my Saihu, if all of these old, worn things weren't mine, then I had absolutely no idea where I'd come to – no clue as to how this place was connected with me.

Hurriedly, Mum unloaded the motorbike and began sifting through what she had bought. At the same time, she wrestled with Chouchou. He seemed to have surmised she had something for him. He was overly excited and impatient at the same time, nipping at her arms as she dug around through the items on the ground. Finally, she pulled out two great ham sausages.

Mum distributed the gifts and then quickly went to let the chickens out. I followed after her as though I were her tail. More memories returned. I recognised the blue-painted pieces of plywood that now helped to enclose the chicken coop. They used to form one of the shelves in Mum's shop. And then I sighed... the air released from my lungs as if I'd been holding it for much too long. This place... home... I could feel its roots regrowing in my heart, quietly, with just a touch of sorrow. I asked Mum where the firewood was. I'd get the dinner started.

THE DOG THAT CARRIED RICE

Mum had returned to her sunflower fields immediately after Granny's funeral, whereas I had lingered in the town for several days. She'd been worried about Saihu, who had been confined to the yurt for too many days as it was. Of course, Mum had left her enough food and water – that wasn't the problem. It was just that Saihu was such a cowardly little dog. She'd always been with and around people, and had never wandered far beyond home. But now she had been left alone, barred inside the yurt; not just for a day, but for several. Mum had had to go home.

There had been Chouchou to think of too. Much bigger than Saihu, much wilder too, there was no way he could've been tied up anywhere, and leaving him inside the yurt with Saihu had certainly been out of the question. No, there had been no other option but to leave him outside to fend for himself.

She had had to think about the chickens and the rabbits as well, both of which had been locked up for days. They all needed to be let loose, to breathe a bit of fresh air.

And then she had waited for me to return. It's why we raced back from the commune like we did. Once I was back, life could return to what it had been. Routine resumed. Granny was gone, but life hadn't really seemed to change that much.

Mum would end up making dinner, even though I had started the fire. It was something simple – rice porridge with some of the vegetables she'd bought in the commune fried up as a side dish. The taste was a little strange, however, for she stir-fried the veg for what seemed like ages and then added quite a bit of sticky chilli bean paste. Perhaps stranger still was that they were delicious.

I kept eating, and as I did, something occurred to me: this was perhaps the first time I had ever really enjoyed the food Mum had cooked. And what's more, everyone else seemed to be in agreement. This was the best food she'd ever made – it reminded me of delicious braised pork, sweet and sour fish... there was a touch of roasted tofu about the taste; egg fried rice, hot and sour soup with wontons – it was amazing. Now, it is true that nearly every mother has her own speciality, or at least every child has memories of their Mum making their favourite food, but it was my granny who raised me more than Mum... Sort of... I mean, I did spend a lot of time with Mum when I was young, but I can't recall her ever making me a meal that was so good. Mum was actually better known for making terrible food, despite the fact that she would eat what she made with great relish. It was an inside joke, so to speak, that whoever was staying with her was bound to suffer great misfortune, at least when it came time to eat.

It's true. The only memories I have of eating her food when I was young are those that saw me unable to endure half of what she made. It was always just so awful. Mum was of course oblivious to all of this, instead believing we loved whatever she made... and that we had to empty our bowls no matter what. Fortunately, Granny was there. That's not to say she was anything but rough around the edges – in fact, she was as rough and ready as her daughter – but it was never a chore to eat her food, at least not for me. Thinking of her now and the food she used to make, the roast potatoes and string beans, deep-fried dumplings, wonton soup, lotus root soup with pork ribs... Ah just thinking of it brought a warm and satisfied feeling to my stomach.

I kept eating the meal Mum had prepared, and as the bottom of the plate became easier to see, I could also feel a... a presence alongside me... vague and unclear, but there nevertheless... for a moment... Granny had come back... at least, that's what I felt. Who knows really... perhaps it was Granny's death that had relieved Mum of that quality that had made her so hard in the past...

Once we'd finished eating, Mum and I took some time to discuss the days... and plans... ahead. This was her second year out here, and she considered herself much more experienced. Indeed, compared to the previous year, she told me, there was much less to worry about this year, even when it came to the day-to-day chores or going back and forth between the yurt and the field. She'd reseeded the field multiple times and managed to get four yields of sunflowers from the land. There were about ten acres left to take care of, but those had begun to sprout little flowers. Yes, the new growth was sparse and uneven as though the plants were struggling to cling onto life in the deep wilderness they found themselves in. But it was new growth nonetheless.

Out of all of the families in the area, we were the only one that was responsible for a plot of land that didn't even amount to a hundred acres. Everyone else had far, far more – some over a thousand acres – and the rest had at least two or three hundred. To make things even more challenging for us, the land we had could only be considered the worst of the worst, the leftover scraps on the edge of the desert. In spring, when it was time to turn over the earth, the large, many horse-powered tractor would be lent to us, but the driver was never happy about working our land, feeling it was more of a hassle than anything else. As a result, he would cut corners and really only do a half-arsed job. Being on the edge, as we were, also meant we received water last – and disaster first.

"Everybody says it," Mum complained. "There's no water left... these last ten acres are going to be ever so hard to look after." And then she sighed, long and hard. "We're out here on the rim, hard up against the desert, and there's no water... but I'll be damned if the area around the reservoir isn't practically bursting! I heard, too, that they weren't all that careful when they did water the land nearest it; they wasted a lot... but you know what, they only ended up drowning their sunflowers... about half of them were seedless. I'll tell you one more thing... even if it seems like there's no way we can save the crop, I sure as hell ain't going to give up!"

It made sense to shift our energies to the land closer to where the reservoir was.

Good fortune would shine on us that year, however. On both plots, too – the one managed by Mum and the other by Uncle. During that first year when they undertook to seed about two hundred acres together, they'd put themselves in a riskier situation should disaster strike, as it so often did up here. As a result, when things went to pot, everything was destroyed and they both lost out. The following year, they didn't put all their eggs in the same basket, and so things worked out better. Mum took charge of ninety acres, whereas Uncle relocated further up the river to till just over a hundred nearer the hydro station that sat adjacent to the reservoir.

Of course, given the proximity of that bit of land to the source of water for the entire region, the usage fees for it were much, much higher than what Mum was paying, even though there were some greater assurances of a successful yield. Strangely enough, investment in the upper reaches of the river was comparatively low. The land, it seemed, had a reputation for being risky, for being a gamble that could end up leaving one waiting on heaven for the next meal. The question that followed was why anyone would take the risk, but I guess the answer to that was fairly easy: the greater the risk, the greater the reward. Getting rich overnight had its appeal, after all.

I remembered that the year before, two young Kazakhs had tended the land next to where Mum was. About five hundred acres in total. The two men had done well for themselves, benefiting from favourable weather conditions in the years up to the last one and thus earning quite a bit of cash. Indeed, such was their financial strength that they had had enough money to purchase a rather large and impressive tractor. Later on, the government announced changes to shepherding practices, and thus the two of them went off to Beijing to attend the requisite general meeting on model labour.

They were both very young, and suddenly very rich. And very committed to the approach they had employed. Consequently, when things turned sour and the inevitable hardships struck, it was very difficult for them to just give up. Mum was the same. She believed wholeheartedly in what she was doing. She was also firm in the belief that if they or someone else could get rich out here, so could she. And if others lost, well, there was no need for her to dread the same happening to her. Her mantra summed up this determination: "What makes me different from them?"

I remember Granny used to love telling stories about the dog that carried rice.

Ages ago, when the great flood submerged the land, those who were fortunate, man and beast, were able to ford their sunken homes and arrive at a strange new land. They hadn't been able to bring anything from the old world into the new, so in essence they had to start over from scratch. But they had no seeds since they'd all been lost on the rolling waves that had flooded the land for what seemed like an age. Needless to say, the people fell into great despair. And just when there seemed to be no hope, one of the survivors discovered a single grain of rice on one of the few dogs they'd rescued. One seed, nothing more, but hope in the future rekindled. The story was that the dog had kept its tail erect and out of the water, which, in turn, had enabled the seed to hang on, relatively dry. It thus narrowly escaped the drowned fate of its compatriots, and its accidental resilience changed the destiny of man. Or so the story went.

At the dinner table, Granny was always fond of picking up a grain or two of rice and showing them to Saihu, telling her that this was the rice the little dog had brought. She was also fond of occasionally grabbing Saihu's tail to see if any grains of rice were holding on, disguised as blisters or other bumps under the fur. Never discovering any, however, she would mumble to herself about how a dog's tail doesn't easily blister, how its colour doesn't easily match... and then she would wonder how Saihu remained so white when her tail had not.

Granny was really quite mesmerised by this story. She'd also told it to us a great number of times, far more than I can count. I suppose it was because she felt so grateful to our canine friends for allowing civilisation to continue, and at the same time felt a pang of sorrow that our good fortune relied so heavily on them. A single dog had saved humankind, all with a tail it had kept out of the water. There was, I suppose, something sad and unsettling about the tale... I'm not sure.

As I walked along one of the sunflower fields, a strip of land on the verge of being abandoned, my mind was drawn back to the beginnings of human society, the stories of their innumerable challenges, the difficulties they faced in their early efforts to cultivate the land, their strength and their perseverance. Then I looked up into the sky and thought the universe doesn't care a whit if man survives or not.

Granny was dead. A drop in the ocean of humanity now swallowed up. A quiet life consumed and erased as though it had never existed in the first place. But she had been satisfied with the life she'd lived. She'd fulfilled the smallest and yet the most essential of all tasks: she'd borne and raised children, and she'd left the deepest impression on them, a lasting memory that would stretch thousands of years into the future, passed on as stories to generation after generation. I guess that's how life carries on, how civilisations continue.

She'd spent the entirety of her life pulling on the weakest of mooring ropes in this world. I'd seen these ropes, too, billions of them hauling the heaviest of ships, slowly but inexorably moving them forward. Two dogs followed behind her, unhurried but never falling too far behind. The plains were empty and quiet. Four lizards squirmed around underfoot, deftly sidestepping my feet. I knelt down, patted Saihu's head and ruffled her ears. Her eyes were bright crystal globes that seemed to reflect the universe. She hadn't realised Granny was dead. She didn't know. Her heart was filled with a hope I couldn't understand. She would forever continue to wait. I could hold my tongue no longer.

"Tell me, Saihu, the rice you've brought... Where is it?"

At the southern reaches of the sunflower fields, desert sands ebbed and flowed. In the north, the Gobi stood hard and unrelenting, flat black stones mixed in with the desert sand. There were no trees and no people. Clouds danced and swirled through the sky as rivers cut and flowed over the ground. At dusk, the entire landscape shimmered in a brilliance that could be seen nowhere else. One could stand here ten thousand times, and still the senses would feel something new. It was home to a perfect loneliness. In that place, in whatever moment of time, one's worries and cares would all be washed away. A sublime experience of simply... being there, I suppose.

The sunflowers in those remaining ten acres were few and far between, their stems weak and vulnerable, easy victims of the blowing wind. But still they held on. And when their flowers bloomed to varying dimensions – some big, some small – they created an unparalleled romantic scene. I knew then, realised immediately, that these flowers possessed an overwhelming beauty, a golden radiance that emanated in all directions. A glorious, grand scene indeed.

That was as long as they could last out here in this wilderness.

A dog bark stirred me from my trance. A larger one was chasing a smaller one, racing past me and off to the west. As my eyes followed them, they fell, too, on the image of a person far off on the horizon, a figure standing against the setting of the sun. I turned my head and saw Mum. Her naked form gradually rose up from the ground. She'd been pulling weeds as usual, but now she straightened and walked slowly, calmly towards the yurt. Then she faded away for a moment, only to reappear fully clothed. The size of her figure had grown with the decreased distance.

The scarecrow we'd just erected, despite there being no crows to speak of, stood watch in between us, if only off to the side. Once we left this land, it would watch over our abandoned fields.

A sudden wave of excitement, fear and passion rose up in my

throat. But no words came out. The moment passed, and I yelled out to Saihu and Chouchou. My whistle was shrill and ear-shattering. It was as though I were calling to every beast under the sky, beckoning them all to come to me. At the same time, it seemed like I was beseeching them, promising them the world. I was there, standing alone, my entreaties proof that in that moment, in that place, I existed, however weak I may be.

18

SCARECROW

It's true. The first task Mum gave me after I returned home was to make the scarecrow. Not to frighten crows or other birds, mind you, but to scare the gazelles away from the sunflower fields. It was a prop, nothing more... but out here on the edges of the Gobi, would I be able to find the rice straw to make one? Even regular straw would be hard to come by.

I remember walking up and down the small river canal searching for straw, but all I found was a cracked plastic basin, two worn and empty sacks that used to contain fertiliser, and a few empty bottles of agrichemicals.

To make dinner out here in the wilderness usually required a fair bit of coal. We might have had a can of butane, too, maybe a couple of cans, but they were only to be used in emergencies, and if you could get by without using them at all, so much the better. There was also firewood, which we'd drag along with us whenever we moved. But its most important use was to get the fire started rather than actually cook a meal since it would burn out faster and we didn't really have that much. I recall shifting through the wood, turning pieces over as I looked for a few longer pieces. My plan was to use them for the scarecrow's body. Finally, I managed to scrounge enough wood to make a figure just over an average man's height, with an arm span perhaps a little longer than normal. It looked more like a cross than anything else. Certainly not a scarecrow.

But Mum had ordered me to make one, and so I did. The two sacks I had found would serve to give the phoney man a torso. The cracked plastic basin would be his head. The only problem was that it looked nothing like a man. To try and remedy this… problem… I sifted through Mum's old aprons and found one I thought I could use. Then I searched through her old, knotty and worn wool sweaters. These, in turn, were put on the haphazard scarecrow to give him a little extra girth.

It was a marked improvement over his first iteration.

However, the more I looked at him, the more he appeared to be amiable and rather friendly – a sort of unassuming chap. I wondered whether he would be able to frighten the gazelles… or anyone else for that matter. That's when the empty agrichemical bottles came in handy. I affixed one to each wooden arm, lashing them on tightly with some hemp rope. Satisfied that I could do no more, I stood this rather ridiculous and not altogether imposing scarecrow outside the yurt, waiting there for Mum's inspection. The chickens found him to be terribly interesting, and their curiosity drew them close. Cluck, cluck, cluck, they pecked and milled about where his feet ought to have been as though they were in heated discussion about the scarecrow's effectiveness. Chouchou showed up not too long after. I remember he sniffed once and then jumped up onto the hapless fake man, knocking him over. But he wasn't attacking him. No, he crooked his head under the scarecrow's arm and fell fast asleep. Mum's old wool sweater was rather cosy, I suppose. It no doubt smelled of her, too.

Mum didn't say a word about the scarecrow after she first saw him. Instead, she walked straight past, marching purposefully towards the rear of the yurt. A moment later, she re-emerged and strode over to the fake man I'd constructed. She tied a rather bright – one could say gaudy – necklace made of used plastic bags beneath the scarecrow's chin. Then she pulled the cloth that had served as a curtain for the dog's den and wrapped that around the phoney man's shoulders as a cloak. A cape, that's what it was, or at least intended to be. Finally, she stood him up next to the yurt.

What could I say? The additions Mum made to his garb allowed the scarecrow to cut an impressive figure against the landscape. He was a man, however fake, that would've caused no small amount of uproar amongst the children, if there were any nearby. At the very least, he would surely snatch the attention of any strangers – man or beast – that happened by.

The following morning, we transported our new family member out into the sunflower fields and sunk him deep into the earth, making sure he wouldn't topple over. Once erect, Mum straightened out his clothes one last time before shouting into the wind, ostensibly for the gazelles to hear. "Don't ever come round here, do you hear me, if you're hungry, find somewhere else to eat – someone else's home. The Liu family to the east are well enough off! Go and bother them!"

Satisfied with our creation, we turned to depart. Then, after we'd walked a few metres, I turned and stared back at the scarecrow. I could see him towering just above the sea of sunflowers, his cape billowing behind him in the wind. He looked rather absurd, but I couldn't deny there was a certain type of majesty about him... an indomitable quality that spoke its warning: no trespassing.

It was hard to say whether or not the scarecrow would be all that effective against the gazelles, but what was unmistakable was that we all slept better knowing he was out there. It was really quite strange. In the past, Chouchou would often spend the night barking madly at sounds in the dark, but that first night with our new friend standing watch, the night was ever so quiet. Indeed, it seemed as though – to me at least – we were adrift in a great boundless, silent emptiness... with the scarecrow at the centre... a lonely, circular island afloat underneath the moon's glow... a great circular disc beyond the gazelles' line of sight...

I remember sinking into the deepest of deep sleeps after that.

When morning came, I knew I had to go and see him. The sun was rising over the horizon, and its warm rays of light shone on my back and pushed me forward. I felt as though my body was under someone else's control. Soon, the scarecrow came into sight and grew larger and larger as I got closer and closer. He was standing as we left him, unmoving, the sun reflecting off his multicoloured garb. A man alone in the world.

I wondered then what he had experienced that first night in the field. Yesterday had been his birthday – his first one – but already he was much older than I. He was standing there firm, quiet and resolute. No doubt he had seen much, but there were no words forthcoming. No stories would he tell. I took out my phone and snapped a picture. The scene was perfect. In that moment, at that angle, it looked very much as though the scarecrow was supporting the entire blue sky above him. In that rectangular frame, he was the meeting point between heaven and earth – the sky was open wide, the earth was a sprawling expanse, the air was clear, and the sunflowers rose in awesome chorus. It was as though the shutters to some secret world had been thrown open and there stood the scarecrow, his head tilted towards the sky...

But once I clicked off my mobile phone, the door to that world closed. The sunflowers became still again, each petal and leaf unmoved and unmoving. Only the plastic bottle on the scarecrow's arm continued to tremble in the slight morning breeze.

The photo I'd taken was sooooo beautiful, leaving me quite impressed with my mobile phone and the camera it possessed. I paid only about four hundred yuan for it, and yet still it had such a great camera. It was a pity then when sometime later I lost it. There'd be no more pictures like the one I'd taken. I guess I should've been happy I'd copied the image onto a flash drive before losing my phone. In fact, I was really grateful I had... up until the time I dropped my flash drive and broke it... I'd stupidly put it high up on a bookshelf.

Ah... but I guess I was still grateful, I knew the scarecrow was out there, standing guard... just as he was in the photo that was there in those broken pieces of my flash drive, his arms outstretched, his ever watchful gaze on the boundless green land that rolled out beneath his feet...

But there'd been no witnesses.

When that marvellous scene had played out, Mum had been busy in the yurt. Saihu had been sunbathing. The path that was our dirt road was only about a third of a metre wide. In this human world of ours, it was perhaps only the Forever Red Commune that had disappeared quicker than us. Minibuses came and went. People left and sometimes returned. Slowly, slowly their hearts changed. The world underfoot has existed for aeons, but all I had were a few dozen years... and one mobile phone. When miracles happened, hope would outweigh loneliness, and there was little else to do but cry... Life is made up of things that have never happened before, and they will never happen again. After the miracle of that scene, only the scarecrow remained, gently looking down on me. In all directions, the sunflowers continued to grow, quiet and serene, our hopes for the future bound up with them... and him.

19

MOTHER EARTH

Lizards, I feel, are the single most similar creature to Mother Earth. Their ability to remain motionless, disguised amongst the myriad masses of animals populating the planet, serves to make their silence a concentrated single drop of all that is wild and untamed. It's that capacity to conceal themselves in the moment that is the source of the world's brightness, its grandness. At least it is to me.

I remember the day. The intensity of the sun at noon was opening up the winter recesses of Mother Earth, burning off the darkness and cold from the night before. I removed my shoes to stand barefoot on the firm, hard earth underneath. I stood there for what seemed like forever... I... lingered. But I couldn't hope to match the lizard's ability to do the same. I guess that's what makes us different... Mother Earth and I... estranged strangers. But I remember... standing like that... under the light of the world... it felt as though a thousand eyes were staring at me and there was nowhere to hide. All I could do was search for traces of the... the lizard... Time ceased to pass, and I remained there, unconcealed, so many eyes staring at me and yet, somehow, someway, I was able to endure the attention.

And in that moment, I found that I could suddenly say all those things I'd been too shy to say before. I could talk of 'love' and 'attachment'. I was no longer plagued by human stubbornness, aloofness. In their place, I felt a sense of kinship with people. I felt clean and honest, pure. And like those people, I felt love for my home, for the day-to-day realities of living, the complicatedness and the messiness of it all, the contradictions and weight that went with it.

But there was absolutely nothing that could make the lizard move. It remained motionless, not but two or three feet away. The sun bore down on it, unobstructed. No shadow, no respite. The creature was laid bare in the sun, or perhaps it's better to say it had concealed itself under the sun's glare. There's a particular fierceness about the shape of the lizard's body. But also a certain form of tenderness about it, too. Its eyes looked as though they were always filled with tears. I watched it, but it did not watch me. I stared at it, my eyes unwavering, but it never once reciprocated, never once directed its gaze... at me.

The sun burned white hot. I straightened myself and closed my eyes. When I opened them again, the world had turned the page, there was something different... barely noticeable... the lizard had arched its tail into the air. It was as though it was dreaming. The appendage continued to reach into the sky, although at a speed hardly visible to the naked eye. Ever so slightly, bit by bit, its tail grew longer and reached further and further.

I blinked then, a number of times, trying to refocus my line of sight. The reptile's tail had begun to curve ever so slowly around itself, gradually working its way towards its head, seemingly determined to wrap around its tiny torso before finally coming to a halt. Its tail had become an impenetrable barrier protecting its vital regions.

Its defence prepared, the lizard now angled its head upwards and trained its ears on whatever sounds it could. Fortunately for me, I remained beyond the range in which it could hear and identify. I was a powerless observer, reduced to using my strength to futilely push against an unbreakable glass barrier. Not only was I prevented from doing more, I was also imprisoned. I thought to scream, but no sooner had the idea popped into my mind than I was forcibly thrust outside this world of living things, beyond the realm of hearing for this little creature.

In this arid place, the wilderness marches ever forward, the earth slow and heavy, the sky above light and graceful. And yet despite its girth, still it moves, always to the future, gradually losing its weightiness to become as lithe and nimble as the air. I feel myself carried up with it. But the blueness is not as welcoming as it seemed; it grows hard and heavy at my approach, imposing its own weight on me. Only the sun remains unchanged, forever above, its gaze forever elsewhere.

My mind then suddenly drifts to the inland sea that was once the Gobi. This vast, desolate expanse is the denouement of a great tragedy that played out in this land aeons ago. It's the reason why people still say: "... until the end of days, the world continues to change..." When that time comes, when the end draws near, all oaths and promises will fail.

I stooped to examine a blade of grass more carefully. Its colour seemed dull, its health in question, and yet it was still delicate and fine. I brushed away the sand and dust that clung to it, fully revealing its deep shade of green, exquisite like polished jade. All of this – the end of everything – had always been thus, but no one had ever thought to pay it any attention before. I was the only one who had taken things to heart – the only one who had internalised this pain as though it were my own.

The world goes on, marching towards... what? I walked on too... on and on... my mind a jumble of thoughts... if I removed my shoes, would my feet grow roots into the earth? If I were naked, would my limbs grow leaves?

The more I walked, the more I could feel the earth's heart, its gravitas, its *gravity* pulling me down. It grew harder and harder to lift my feet from its surface. I struggled against being absorbed into its embrace, from being transformed into a seed.

Seeds in a flowerpot can only blindly grope in the dark. Like an old lady's hand clenched tightly to a cane, they search in all directions without ever seeing anything, carefully extending feelers before retracting them again. Their ears listen... attentive to all sounds. During the day, they hide, concealed deep in the earth, waiting for night to fall so that they can procreate and grow. The seeds buried deep in the earth have no such fear; you call, I shall answer, rise and fall, each struggling to be the first, fearful of losing out, the need for roots to wind and wend their way through the soil, to push and fight for life, a great orchestric concatenation of being.

People have come. Their footsteps fall on the earth, and the plants exhale slowly together, urging each other to be silent before they all hold their breath. They wait for the footsteps to pass them before coming to life once again. Only in man's absence can the world feel at ease. Flowers bloom when man is elsewhere. They snatch the moment of time when they're free from human presence. Leaves unfurl when man departs, and close just as quickly when he returns. If it's true that nature flourishes only in the depths where single rays of light reach, then humanity's trundle across this earth is the extinguishing of that light.

Man's footfalls dig deep into the soil.

On those occasions when Mum strode off into the farthest reaches of the sunflower fields, her shadow was pulled out behind her, long and dark, solitary and alone. It's as though she were dragging the weight of the world in her wake – the most important people, the most fatigued.

At the edges of the world, two healthy and strong, beautiful and vibrant Mongolian gazelles chase each other around, disappearing out of sight over one horizon only to appear on another. An eagle circles in the sky. A silky wind blows. Granny is here too, tottering somewhat unsteadily over the uneven landscape, a bag in her hand. From time to time, she bends over. I know she's collecting cow patties. They're for the fire to keep her warm. Saihu is there as well, bounding about excitedly, waiting for her chance to race off home with Granny. I knew it was her, when she was but a young dog. I knew, too, that what I was seeing happened many, many years ago. I wondered if this had been the same place Mum had telephoned me from, the land she'd seen out of the storm. The reception had been so good that it was ironic when she couldn't put things into words.

She'd looked every which way, but in each direction the far-off sunflower fields withered. Then her eyes fell on a place even further away, a herd of gazelles were trying to evade a pursuing motorcycle. The sky was a brilliant indigo shade. There was no sign of rain.

Mum sighed. "When are you coming home?"

Up till now, I've not been able to answer her.

There was nowhere for me to escape. I continued to search the area for lizards.

The lizard chose not to appear.

20

THE ESSENCE OF TROUBLE

Taking stock of everything, Chouchou's deficiencies far
outweighed his positive attributes – he had a vicious temperament,
an insatiable appetite, a horrible memory, he snapped at Saihu
regularly, and he wouldn't stop chasing the chickens. And if that
wasn't enough, he loved stealing shoes. No, that's not right. It's
better to say he loved collecting shoes – that's the only way to
explain the pile of 'found' footwear to the rear of our yurt. Chouchou 'collected' them from across the ten thousand acres of tilled
land.

Once people began to realise that Chouchou was responsible for
their missing footwear, we'd have visitors every few days, noticeably barefoot, in search of their shoes. We'd direct them to the pile
in the back, and then they'd begin sifting through as though they
were at some police station with a lost-and-found box in front of
them. Chouchou would never be far off either. Usually, he'd
watched them look for the shoes, basking in the sunlight, wagging
his tail as they did so, assuming a posture of feigned indifference.

Not only did Chouchou enjoy pilfering other peoples' shoes and
bringing them home with him, he was also quite fond of taking our
shoes and depositing them at our neighbours' places. It was a rather
perplexing hobby to say the least. Mum was the first to discover his

peculiar habit. It happened early one morning when she awoke and realised she was missing a shoe. Out in this expansive, flat, wide-open wilderness, it took great effort to actually lose anything. What's more, the fact that the missing item was a torn and tattered old shoe, well, it wasn't exactly something you would think people would be keen to steal. I remember she looked up and down, under every rock and behind every piece of furniture – or pile of rubbish – around our yurt but found nothing. It was when she was about to give up that she began to realise what was going on.

A neighbour showed up. He was a labourer who worked the adjacent field – a youngish Kazakh boy about nineteen years old. His home was about a kilometre away, or thereabouts. He'd come with a much-worn shoe in his hand and asked if it was hers. Mum just stared at him at first, a puzzled and confused look on her face. He continued: "Dog... yours... bring... my house..." Speaking Chinese wasn't exactly his strong suit. Not fully understanding what he was saying, Mum could not deny that the young Kazakh indeed had her shoe. All she could do was offer her thanks. But the young man wouldn't leave, nor did he say goodbye, even after handing back her shoe. Instead, he stood there silent for what seemed like half a day, before bashfully trying to speak Chinese again: "Auntie... my... shoe... look you... my shoe..."

That's when Mum noticed he wasn't wearing anything on his feet.

For us, this was the first experience of this kind of situation. For him, it was the second. On that initial occasion, he was as perplexed as Mum had been, wondering who in the world – or at least out here in the wilderness – would steal his shoe? He never found it either, so finally he was left with no choice but to throw away the other shoe. After all, what's the point of working in the fields with only one foot covered? Better to go barefoot, he thought, which is what he had been doing.

Some days later, he was on the road transporting a container of agrichemicals when he passed by our yurt. His eyes fell on Chou-chou relaxing in the sun. And in his maw, he noticed, was his shoe, which Chouchou was happily chewing on. He'd stopped almost immediately and challenged Chouchou for his footwear, finally winning it back after a brief struggle. With one shoe in hand, the man had searched for its partner, the one he'd thrown away, but unfortunately he couldn't find it. He did, however, stumble upon Mum's shoe. Hence his visit.

Mum was both embarrassed and angry. She cursed Chouchou for his impudence and then escorted the boy around the back to help look for his missing shoe. This was the first time Mum had noticed Chouchou's secret stash. It was an impressive display of footwear… men's and women's, single shoes and pairs, new and old.

It was as though, in that moment, Mum saw all the many men and women, young and old, working the fields in bare feet…

Her head swam. Then, with great humility, she instructed the young man to spread the word… if shoes were to go missing or had already disappeared, it was likely Chouchou had taken them. Thereafter, whenever a shoe vanished, those living closest to us – it didn't matter who – knew the first place to look. Our neighbours also took appropriate action to prevent Chouchou's attacks on their footwear in the future: before settling in for the night, they made sure to bring them all inside with them.

Mum took to hanging hers up, high enough so that Chouchou could not reach them.

Unfortunately for the young Kazakh, however, he wasn't able to find his shoe amongst the ones Chouchou had been hoarding. Mum gave him twenty yuan as compensation, and as an apology. It was too bad, then, that the money wasn't of much use. After all, it couldn't be stuck to the soles of his feet to serve as shoes, could it? And out here in the wilderness, well, there was really nowhere to buy a new pair. These thoughts, however, he kept to himself.

Besides Chouchou's penchant for pinching shoes, the rascal also enjoyed chasing the chickens. He wouldn't eat them once he'd caught them – he wouldn't even bite them. Instead, it was more as though he were a child grasping his favourite doll, like a human holding something tight to the breast – that's how Chouchou treated the chickens. And once he had them so embraced, his long and incredibly wet tongue would extend and shower them in salvia... It wasn't long before the poor creature would be drenching wet and shivering.

We witnessed this rather humorous performance twice. On the first occasion, the chicken died from fright... or perhaps it drowned... we couldn't be sure. The second time it happened, Mum reacted more quickly and rescued the fowl from Chouchou's wet embrace. Unfortunately, the trauma of the experience prevented it from ever laying another egg.

Chouchou had also tried this with the rabbits. He'd pin them to the ground, then lick their fur one way, before licking it back. The rabbits being subjected to such abuse could only squirm a little before growing limp. Unable to jump away or otherwise extricate themselves, they were forced to endure the humiliation.

Chouchou's sole contribution to Mum's enterprise was to chase away the gazelles, which he excelled at, it should be said. During that difficult first year when the entire area was struck with natural disaster after natural disaster, when the gazelles had arrived like a swarm of locusts to prey on our fields, it only took Chouchou a second to see the invading forces before he would fly into action and begin driving them off. On those occasions, Mum couldn't help but smile, gratified by Chouchou's diligence in protecting the sunflowers. Of course, there was also a less than welcome outcome of these chases: Chouchou invariably trampled down as many sprouting sunflower plants as the gazelles munched. To make matters worse, the encouragement Mum gave Chouchou for his heated pursuit of the gazelles only egged him on to even greater destructiveness for he soon took to chasing anything on four legs, including herds of sheep.

To exacerbate the matter further, in spring, the path that lay adjacent to our field became the main route for the nomadic herdsmen to traverse on their way into the mountains. As soon as their animals came into sight, Chouchou's eyes would sparkle with great anticipation for the chase to come. A moment later, he would fling himself full force into the procession of sheep, bounding every which way, howling as he did so and causing no small amount of consternation amongst the shepherds and their livestock. Unsurprisingly, the herd would scatter in all directions, adding even more fuel to the burning fires in the breasts of the shepherds.

It would take the better part of a day for the herdsmen on horseback to gather in all of their sheep.

Mum could only stand by helplessly and witness the chaos wrought by her favourite companion. She had tried to rein him in, she'd hollered after him, she'd flung her fists and feet in his direction, but all to no effect. Chouchou was lost in the heat of the moment, unable to stop, even if he might've wanted to. Finally, to save what face she could, Mum would resort to ignorance, pretending not to know who the dog's keeper was.

Ah, Chouchou. What a scamp and a torment. Mum couldn't help but love him, despite the trouble he caused. Indeed, if he was missing but for half a day, she would be terribly worried and fretful that something had happened to him.

The drought that year had been especially bad, and as a result the pump house located at the upper reaches of the river had exhausted its limited supply of water well before many of the fields had been irrigated. As Mum's sunflowers became increasingly parched, as their petals fell to the ground with greater and greater frequency, her concern grew and grew. So, too, did her anger. Finally, and after great difficulty, water did arrive, and the fields could be irrigated. Unfortunately, at the same time, Chouchou disappeared.

I remember that morning. There was no sign of Chouchou, but since work would not wait, Mum had to go out into the fields. I could see her out there, watering the sunflowers and casting her eyes in every direction, hoping to catch sight of him. She called out for him too, desperately praying her voice would carry in the wind and call that great canine nuisance back home. When lunch came and went, and still Chouchou had not returned, Mum's imagination played havoc on her mood and tormented her heart greatly. To compound matters even more, the fields needed to be irrigated, and thus no one could be spared to go and look for him. After all, we had very little water to begin with, and the dykes and embankments were constantly giving way and causing water to be wasted. We had to prevent this at all costs. Searching for Chouchou would simply have to wait.

That's not to say that Mum wasn't conflicted. Several times, she thought to stop the work she was doing and go and find her dog. The work, she thought, could be continued after he was home. But I knew she wouldn't do this. She couldn't. We had already waited so long for the water in the first place. If we gave it up now, the farmers further down the river would be only too happy to use what was ours to irrigate their own fields. Still, she couldn't be blamed for feeling the way she did. In that moment, it was as though that blasted beast, that pest that often caused more trouble than he was probably worth, was more important than the life-and-death work we had to get done.

There was another time when Chouchou got Mum all worked up and worried. It happened when my uncle, who was tending the land up nearer the reservoir, had paid her a visit. Or rather, it happened when he left. For some unknown reason, that stupid dog got it into his head to chase after my uncle's motorbike. I don't know why – nobody did – but Chouchou ended up running after him for several dozen kilometres. He ran so hard, in fact, that it wasn't long before his paws were turned into bloody stumps more than anything else. He was leaving a trail of bloody prints behind him, and yet he wouldn't give up.

Mum was really upset after we did finally get him home. She was angry at his impulsiveness, but worried, too, about the state of his paws. The only recourse, or so she thought, was to give him shoes to wear – two pairs. Of course, Chouchou wasn't exactly grateful for the footwear, and about thirty minutes later he'd already kicked them off. That's when Mum cursed my uncle, wondering why he hadn't slowed his bike and let Chouchou trot along beside him. That way, at least, he wouldn't have injured himself so severely. Never one to back down, Uncle only retorted in anger about Chouchou's general penchant for bad behaviour, before sarcastically wondering if Mum knew what kind of dog she had. "Do you know, huh, what kind of animal you've raised? Do you suppose he's well enough behaved to ride along with me?" Ironically, it was something we had never tried.

Afterwards, however, Uncle had little choice but to relent. Chouchou continued to chase him whenever he visited, and so there was nothing else he could do but reduce his speed in order to prevent the dim-witted animal from hurting himself again. Indeed, so slow did he have to go that he could've pushed his bike just as quickly. All for that bloody dog.

"Ah... my Chouchou... he's the best, isn't he?"

"At causing trouble perhaps... I can't think of anything else."

"He can chase away those blasted gazelles."

"Ha... and quite the skill that is!"

"He's never far from my side either..."

21

LONELINESS

For most of her life, Mum's been by herself. She's lived alone. In Akehala, her days revolved around ensuring her personal safety measures were always at the ready: first, she would check the small door – more an emergency exit – that she'd dug out of the rear wall. It was there in case, say, a stranger broke in, however unlikely that might've been. But if it did happen, and if that same ne'er-do-well gave chase, well, she had a ladder positioned near the emergency exit for quick access to the roof. And if that same rascal thought to charge up after her, the hammer she had waiting up there would soon make short work of the bastard's skull, and that'd be the end of that...

In addition to these arrangements, Mum had set up other safety measures. For instance, underneath several of the cushions inside, she had tucked away a knife or two, just on the off chance that she was unable to make it to the emergency exit. Behind the main door, she'd stashed limestone and other odds and ends, all countermeasures for any kind of intruder...

Ah... what can I say? She'd watched far too many dramas for sure.

"Maybe so," she would reply to this, "but how can I not be afraid – there's only me."

It's strange putting this into words, I have to say, for it makes Mum seem so timid – a scaredy-cat if ever there was one. Of course, this couldn't be farther from the truth as it was her choice to come out here into the wilderness, to take care of a huge plot of land all on her own. In a sense, out here... in this expanse... her whole life's exposed. I mean, there aren't any walls to hide behind, nor any emergency backdoors, nor ladders or hammers... But since moving out here... she's never once mentioned anything about being afraid.

"What's there to be afraid of?" she answered. "I'm in the middle of nowhere. There's not another person around for kilometres."

There really wasn't anyone else around. Out here on the edge of the Gobi, you could walk for hours without bumping into a soul. It was as though you could walk for millions of years all on your own, never encountering a fellow traveller. And not only were there no people about, there wasn't even any smoke billowing up from the tents you would pass by, nor from the pits that often served the same purpose as a tent. The road ahead, too, was devoid of any signs of previous passage. In all directions, there was only emptiness – the great expanse. Standing on Mother Earth like this, alone, was akin to returning home to a planet that had inhabited the heavens likewise alone for millions of years.

All the world's secrets are in the wind. In its whistle, there's excitement and urgency. But I don't understand a single sentence. It does its utmost to push at me, to grab at me, to let me in on its secrets, but I still cannot understand any of it. Then it spins and swirls away from me, whipping up another gust not too far away, first whirling up towards the heavens, then down towards the earth.

I stood there dumbstruck, feeling greatly as though I'd been away from the earth for far too long.

Then the wind began to dissipate. The earth, ancient in all its glory, stood suspended in the universe, firm and unyielding. And there I stood, too, perched upon the world's tallest point, companion to the stars that leaned towards the cosmos. The sun and moon brushed against my shoulder and then continued on their march. The earth bobbed atop this great celestial ocean, rolling over its waves, up and down in rhythm with my breathing.

Now... the final and only remaining trace of humanity lay amongst the sunflower fields. The young seedlings pushed up through the soil, reaching straight into the sky, orderly, healthy and strong. I drew close to the field, searching for my mum, as well as Saihu and Chouchou, but I could not find them. It slowly began to dawn on me then: I was the last woman standing; humanity's last remnant. I returned home and walked around the yurt. A chicken suddenly stepped out from behind a pile of earth, its pace slow and unconcerned. It twisted its neck and peered at me. I heaved a gloomy sigh of relief.

"There are times," Mum said, "when I'd like to sing, but then no song comes to mind. Then on other occasions, the lyrics percolate up, and I immediately break out into song. Sometimes I sing for Saihu, other times for the rabbits. Curled up around my feet, Saihu listens attentively. Her eyes gaze up towards my face. Bright, beautiful orbs filled with thousands and thousands of words. The rabbits, on the other hand, scurry about. They pay little attention to my singing, jumping and hopping, their little mouths wiggling under their noses."

But rabbit tails did follow behind her as she walked into the sunflower fields. Their path was incredibly narrow, their field of vision terribly low. The world was big once again, and there, where the rabbits hopped and jumped about, a cave cut deep into the earth, its bottom far beyond what the naked eye could see. Mum towered over the small creatures; they followed obediently, all towards this hidden, serene world that wound its way underneath the earth. When she didn't sing, the mouth of the cave that opened to this place would be obscured, as were its inner depths. Then, when she did sing, the cave itself would vanish. It was the first time the rabbits saw the sky, the first time they saw something that might resemble the ocean.

Physical toil is pure, unadulterated and... quiet. In Mum's heart of hearts, she knew she should be out weeding the fields. She knew they needed watering soon. She knew, too, that she hadn't yet bought the necessary fertiliser. These were the things that populated her life in the wilderness and made it full and busy.

A shovel in hand, her mind lost deep in thought, Mum would walk the breadth of the land, from east to west. Then, abruptly, she would raise her head and spy the most beautiful of clouds hanging in the sky. In an instant, her full and busy life would be rendered apart, split to allow this gigantic mass of whiteness in. A wave of excitement, coupled with a feeling of loss, would wash over her. She would feel a desire to tell the world about this beautiful cloud. But before she could say anything... before she could tell whoever would listen what was on her mind, she stopped to consider how best to say it... And then, as she stood mired deep in thought, the whiter-than-white cloud transformed, lost its splendour and became like any other cloud... But such a change didn't seem to matter to her, for in her words its beauty lived on, and its magnificence grew ever more profound.

Again she thought to sing. But words would not come to mind. At the same moment, she discovered the rabbits had disappeared. Perhaps there was some special, mysterious connection between them and the clouds above. They were both white at least...

Saihu was white, too, but it wasn't her fur, it was her penchant to feel ill at ease, to flee at the first sign of trouble. That's what made her white. She was always and forever a jittery little dog. Mum never let her into the sunflower fields as a result. Her poor legs were bad, after all, and Mum simply didn't have the heart to make her walk more than was necessary.

"You can't come with me, Saihu dear. Stay here and play, I'll be back before you know it."

Saihu understood her words, or at least that's how it appeared for she would never try and follow Mum into the fields – she'd simply curl up on the ground and wait for her return. Still, Mum would turn her head back as she walked away, making sure Saihu was where she was supposed to be. The dog's eyes would follow after her intently, purposefully, but she wouldn't stir – she was too well-behaved for that, despite the grieved, sorrowful look her eyes betrayed. Poor, pathetic Saihu was afraid of the dark, too, terrified of being broken.

I don't know how many times Mum left her like this, or how many times she came back and picked up little Saihu, held her in her arms and walked together deep into the fields, unable to make her wait on her own.

I'd finished making dinner and waited in the yurt for Mum to return. I waited and waited and then fell asleep.

Who's afraid of sleep? It gives us certain insight, allows us to see how weak, feeble and insignificant we are. Sleep is the second most important, most intense thing in this world. Silence is the first.

In my dreams, I stood up, pushed open the door, and strode out into the far-off sunflower fields. I walked for millions of years but did not reach my destination. Millions of years later, I awoke. Dinner was cold, and Mum had still not appeared.

"This place is really quite spectacular," Mum proclaimed as she sat down to eat. "There's no one else around!"

"Then why lock the door when you go out?"

She paused for a few seconds, unable to think of a response. Finally, she offered an answer: "What bloody business is it of yours?"

22

MUM AND UNCLE

Mum had an irritable, and at times violent, temperament. It's just who she was and had always been. I remember one incident in particular when she was still a people's teacher. Needless to say, Mum was as strict as a teacher could be. Indeed, to deal with her unruly charges, she'd implemented, in true Bismarckian fashion, a policy of 'blood and iron', a strict regime of corporal punishment for any and all misbehaving children. Most followed Mum's rules, but there were a few who persisted in acting up, in causing a fuss and being nuisances. As a result, it wasn't long before one of these naughty children ended up receiving a slap on the side of their head for whatever misconduct they were guilty of. Disciplining a student in such a manner was fairly commonplace in those days, but in this case, Mum's actions set off a firestorm. That is, once the child's mother, who was no pushover herself, heard of how her child, her daughter in fact, had been treated, she raced off to the school to confront Mum. Not long after, the two women, right in front of all of the children, began to exchange blows, each pulling savagely on the other's hair, kicking and screaming and hurling such awful language that... well... I cannot repeat here.

By all accounts, it was a rather spectacular scene – I kind of wish I had seen it in person – and one that ultimately caused no small amount of embarrassment for the school's headmaster. It was a pity, then, that the authorities hadn't arrived fast enough to defuse the situation before it became what it did. But nothing could change that, and so it was up to Mum to perform a self-criticism, to apologise in essence, for letting things get out of hand – a teacher should know better, or so the headmaster insisted. Unsurprisingly, Mum refused and instead got into (another) shouting match... this time with her boss. Then she quit, returned home, and decided to take up the life of a farmer. What a temper!

Interestingly, years later it became clear that this was the best thing she could've done. I guess you could say she took to farming like a duck takes to water. Indeed, in terms of cotton, the first crop she planted, her production rates were always far greater than anyone else's. As for the pigs she raised, they were always the heaviest, breaking numerous historical records amongst the work units, year after year. (At the time, Mum was a civilian labourer for the military.)

They say by the age of three you can tell what a child's character will be like when they're a teenager. Then, by the age of seven, you can tell what kind of adult they'll become. When Mum was little, she was not easy to handle, and certainly no soft touch. Her first year in elementary school made that plain enough. For instance, if the boy sitting next to her refused to help her with her schoolwork, she'd hit him so hard he'd end up looking for his teeth on the floor. This remained her modus operandi until she reached middle school when, gradually, her physical strength became less and less a match for the boys. This is not to say she stopped fighting, but rather that she'd lose nine out of ten battles as opposed to winning nearly all of them while in elementary school. The silver lining was that she began to understand what it meant to be afraid and how that could be helpful at times, as well as what the phrase 'grin and bear it' actually meant, at least sort of.

As an adult, married and with a career, she was known as the iron lady for her tough and unyielding approach to work, and for striking fear into those around her. As a direct witness of what kind of wife she made, well, let's say it dissuaded me from ever getting married – I'd seen enough to know it wasn't ever going to be my cup of tea.

But that said, the relationship she had with Uncle was... different... at least according to what I could see. What I mean to say is... she seemed to have had... ulterior motives... That's really the only way to explain why they decided to go ahead and get the marriage certificate... well... sort of.

As I've said before, Mum was a terrible cook. What made things even worse, however, was that this wasn't a source of embarrassment, but rather of pride. Now, a more honourable person might've taken the hint and refused thereafter to make dinner. But not Mum. Or rather, she simply acknowledged she was terrible in the kitchen and then proceeded to say we were all entitled to our own opinions.

"Then can't you learn how to cook a little better... or think of another way to improve upon what you feed us?" We'd asked this question more than once. Her reply was almost always the same: "I don't reckon I've got it in me." We were thus left... with little choice.

As expected, it wasn't even half a year after they'd married that things... happened.

At the time, they should've come to blows, should've had it out. That would've been as... expected. But that's not what happened. They argued, yes, but then Mum telephoned me and asked for my help in... buying menus commonly available in the city... She also grumbled... Uncle had sworn at her something awful, said she was completely useless in the kitchen, and even questioned her womanhood. (Of course, in his mind, a woman *had* to be skilled in the kitchen.) And then, as she grumbled and complained more and more, more and more bile rushed up into her mouth. From my position as an outsider, Mum had married a good number of times, but she'd never been as upset about her abilities in the kitchen, or lack thereof, as she was this time. So I guess you could say... it really was... love.

Without fail, each time Mum washed her face and then applied her facial cream, she'd ruefully lament the growing number of lines across her brow, the wrinkles on her cheeks and neck, the way her skin crinkled around her eyes. "Ah, Da Bao! I've moisturised with you for so many years, and still I've come to this!"

She suspected the cream was too dry, that there was very little difference between using it and not. But there was nothing she could do. She'd used this brand, Da Bao, for years, had had the same jar for what must've been seven or eight years... and still there was some left... She just couldn't throw it away.

Now, on most days, it was true she didn't even use the facial cream. And if she did, it meant there was something happening and that she had to tidy up, which included, of course, her face.

But on one day... I remember she did her best... to look her best... even though there wasn't anything that... important to do... All she had planned was a drive up to the reservoir to scout for new land to cultivate. And she was going to be going on her bike, which meant there'd be wind blowing in her face, dirt and dust kicked up by the tyres... Really not much point in getting all dolled up I figured.

However, she had not only used the cream but also washed her hair! She'd *used* all of that water, which was, considering the usual circumstances, quite exceptional. What's more, she'd put on her best clothes, along with her leather shoes which couldn't help but dazzle (and be really out of place on the steppes). Indeed, she looked stunning, from top to bottom – she'd left behind the usual grey face she wore when doing work in the fields and around the yurt. Her appearance brought to mind another saying: *Out of the chicken coop came a beautiful phoenix.* That was her.

When we finally arrived at our destination, I remember Uncle was already waiting to greet us. He was so excited that he literally bounded over to where Mum had brought the bike to a halt. "Oh my!" he shouted. "Who's this who's come to see me?" That's when it came to me... Finally I understood... and then I cursed myself for being such a fool.

Mum and Uncle would argue two days out of every three. They'd literally be shouting down the heavens – real grudge matches... But then, when they weren't at each other's throats, there were such amorous and happy feelings between them that there couldn't be any discounting their mutual affection.

Mum was garrulous, if not adept at nagging. And Uncle, well, if he wasn't out working, he'd prattle on and on in his own way, too. Actually, he'd never shut up, even when he was out in the fields. "Work's work, isn't it?" he would burble. "What's the point of being hangdog about it?... Eh... just look at that mug! If you really don't want to be out here... then scatter... Who wants to see that wretched scowl of yours anyways?... You know I didn't ask you out here looking like that... Shit... What're you trying to do, make me laugh so much I can't get anything done? Put a smile on your face at least, huh?... Come on now... Can't you show us a few of those pearly whites? And what about them eyes of yours... Look at you squint... eh... That's it... Right there! Like that!... Ah Juan... perfect! You oughta see your face in a mirror... Just look at yerself... ah... You've given this old man quite a laugh... I swear my mouth's curled up like a peapod!"

Of course, these words were usually directed at me.

When he laughed like that, though, I couldn't get over how ugly his face looked. He'd been out in the wind for so, so many years that his eyes looked increasingly slanted, his mouth more and more askew. It wasn't only his face, either, that had been changed by the harsh environment. His hands and feet were rugged, chapped and malformed... They looked nothing like a normal person's appendages... He hadn't had the easiest of lives... There'd been nothing... convenient about it whatsoever.

Take, for instance, his belt.

He'd had it for a dozen years or more, and it was made of fine leather – never any question about its durability. And then, finally, one day when he was out in the sunflower fields, it broke. He knew he'd have to buy a new one at some point, however begrudgingly he felt about it, but he ended up with a strip of canvas to tie his trousers round his waist. Nothing more than what kids might use... although we weren't sure how this had happened. Whatever the reason, he was thereafter forced to make do as best he could, constantly pulling his trousers up and retightening them after even the smallest amount of movement. (Things only got worse in winter when most men and women wore several extra layers, as well as extra trousers, all in the effort to keep warm... Needless to say, the importance of a good belt was even more pronounced then.)

Tying his improvised belt also required particular skill, which added to the nuisance of it all. It was even more difficult to undo. In fact, the more his frustration grew at trying to unfasten his belt, the more it just wouldn't come undone. Eventually, he'd have little recourse but to find Mum and get her to untie it. It would be worse when he ached to go to the toilet. Indeed, on occasions such as these, once loosened he'd simply hold his trousers tightly in hand and then walk, hop and skip his way awkwardly to the toilet. When Mum wasn't around, well, he'd have to clinch his arse as hard as he could and wait for some poor stranger to happen by so that he could ask them for help... Surprisingly, or perhaps because of his age and belief in his own self-importance, he never once felt embarrassed at having to stoop so low – cheeky bastard he was.

I don't know who spread the stories, but sometime after, word got around about his... unique trouser predicament.

The youth where they were living were quite... knowledgeable about things. If they happened to spy Uncle loitering about the public toilet (this was before we were out on the steppes), even if they were some distance off, they'd be sure to come and help him. He was, after all, a well-known old-timer in the town. But they wouldn't come straight away. No... they'd have... fun with him first... and take the most circuitous route possible, thus forcing Uncle to... endure as long as he could.

There was, also, the work in the fields, which was not easy by nature. I didn't help matters by my constant opposition to tilling the land, about which, as I mentioned above, he had more than enough to say. His blood pressure was high, too, and he was prone to bouts of anxiety. He'd experienced paralysis once before, and it'd kept him bedridden for nearly a year. It wasn't easy being a farmer. If nothing else, it was good at taking the wind out of a person, of leaving them exhausted and drained. Tired, worried, given to periodic episodes of total... collapse... Thinking of this... well, who's to say he wasn't daily on the cusp of a stroke... Perhaps he had already had one?

Mum was in the same boat, more or less. She had the same worries... and yet... she still met these risks head-on... with him. Were they two peas in a pod? Or two gamblers addicted to chancing their lives all for the next bet? I couldn't be sure.

The wind would blow something fierce, but the two of them, arm in arm, would support each other and walk on. Their faces would drive into the wind, but they'd meet its challenge head-on and get caked in dust at the same time. Their hair would grow tangled and coarse with sand, but they'd endure these trials, these torments, stoically, as husband and wife. I recall lifting up my camera at times like these, I wanted to snap a picture, but each time, as if on cue, they'd stare back into the lens and grimace... purposefully. In a way, they didn't let things bother them, I suppose, despite the harshness of reality. Or perhaps that was just the image they tried to convey.

CHICKENS

The rooster loved his many mates quite dearly and spent much of his days as though he were on guard, his eyes ever watchful over his harem. At feeding time when the chickens would bustle about and push their way to Mum's feet in anticipation of being fed, the cock would stand at the rear, seemingly content to be as exasperatingly slow as possible, almost unconcerned with being fed. But when they plunged their beaks into the chicken feed and became oblivious to everything else, he would carry on as their sentry, his eyes darting back and forth, scanning the landscape for possible threats. A guard in plainclothes, committed to raising the alarm should danger arise... maybe.

Of course, it was clear he wanted to eat, but his desire was secondary to the task at hand, and so he would stoically stand guard, an exemplar of supreme patience. Maybe. He would stay in this state of readiness, too, until the chickens had finally eaten their fill and gradually begun to saunter off, their appetites satisfied. That's when he would go over to the trough and devour what was left.

He was a skinny rooster. Rather short, too. His feathers lacked a healthy sheen, and bald spots could easily be seen. His tail feathers, often the pride of many cocks, had all fallen out long ago, leaving but a solitary bit of plumage. And if this wasn't sufficient indignity, his comb had long grown withered and taken to drooping over the side of his face. By all outward appearances, he wasn't much of a rooster. At least not until one saw him in action. There was a certain spirit in his eyes, then, an intensity that said he would protect his harem at all costs, the same spirit one maybe read about in the stories of kings and emperors of the past.

This was because, out of all of the chickens Mum had, he was the only cock.

And thus he held his lonely tail feather proudly in the air, he stood guard over his harem, he strolled confidently amongst his concubines and was clearly satisfied with his lot. Maybe.

Out here in the wilderness, Mum raised more than fifty chickens. Her thoughts on this were straightforward enough – she had more than enough space, so why not. And the space wasn't just big, or huge... it was boundless, without borders, fences, or anything else for that matter. Now, one might ask why didn't she raise more chickens, why not five hundred, or five thousand? This is a good question, but the answer is simple: there was only so much chicken feed to go around...

In fact, I opposed Mum's decision to raise chickens, to say nothing about taking care of more. To my mind, fifty were already too many! Each and every day, I had to go out into the fields to scrounge whatever grains I could. They were already a nuisance and a headache. Trying to find feed for more would've killed me. When I first came out here, Mum actually had only ten chickens – the ones she'd brought with her. But with the amount of land she had at her disposal, she soon discovered free-range chickens were much easier to care for. They grew sturdier, were more resistant to disease, and altogether a better investment than having chickens confined to a coop.

When she knew that I was coming home, well, she couldn't just let me lounge about and do nothing – idle hands and all that – so she made sure to purchase several dozen chicks from the village to bring back with her. Eh... I guess it didn't matter that we'd moved out here into the middle of nowhere – we were still a family that raised fowl, more now than ever before.

Mum and Granny really loved the chickens. It's true. Even when we had only about six square metres to our name, we had chickens. We just raised them out in the back of the building. Even when we followed the herdsmen and their flocks, we wouldn't give up our chickens. The only problem was... none of us liked to actually eat chicken, nor did we enjoy the eggs... so why in hell did we raise chickens?

Over the course of a number of years, the municipal government in Akehala, in the interests of aiding herdsmen with settling down, had taken to providing chicks free of charge as a means for them to generate income without roaming the countryside. Since they were free, many took advantage of this, regardless of whether or not they could successfully raise them. It was a 'the more, the better' type of situation. Of course, raising chickens is nothing like tending flocks of sheep out in the wilds, and not a single shepherd had any experience to draw upon. To complicate matters, it didn't take long for many of the herdsmen to become disinclined towards the entire enterprise – as is often the case when things are given away for free – and before much more time passed, eighty to ninety percent of the thousands of chicks gifted were dead. Then, as winter quickly approached, it was assumed the remainder would die, except perhaps for a few – certainly no more than what one could count on one's fingers.

This was exactly what happened, too.

So when the government pushed on with its plan the following year, Mum hung a sign up outside her little store – she still had the shop at that time – saying she would purchase any and all surviving chicks. Naturally, it didn't take long for the townspeople to show up with whatever they had – now those were chickens, let me tell you! They looked like survivors stumbling off the field of some bloody battle, crippled, maimed, but still alive... Indeed most looked more bedraggled and rather closer to death's door than anything else. Some were missing that soft, yellow down from their backs, others from their wings, others still from their breasts. What's more, given that it was summer and they were already in a sorry state, they'd been prime targets for mosquitoes – so much so that red blisters cratered their tiny little bodies, oozing pus and making them look far, far more abject. Survivors from a battlefield indeed! (I should like to add, too, that I had quite a bit of experience with Akehala's mosquitoes. If I were to describe their attacks, I would have to say they swarmed and overwhelmed their victims by sheer numbers. Like great dark clouds of buzzing wings, they would fall upon their prey, relentless, merciless. They were better described as great pulsating storms – hordes of mosquitoes, yes, that's what they were...)

The chicks really were the walking wounded – quite literally – for many of them had even lost their tiny feet, frozen during the winter, blackened by frostbite until all that was left were rounded, malformed stumps. I guess it's not accurate to say they were the walking wounded, for they didn't really walk anymore. They more hopped and toppled over, fluttered their wings to bring themselves back upright, only to crash to the ground again. At night, they couldn't even climb up into their coop for whatever modicum of warmth it might've given them. No, they remained on the frozen earth, lucky to make it to the morning. And if they did, they'd find their tender underbellies with fewer feathers than they had before.

Those who were lucky enough not to have their feet frozen didn't, however, escape the night unscathed. They would, at the least, have a claw or two drop off from frostbite, leaving shortened toes and still deformed feet. Half or more would also lose their combs.

Mum was quite grief-stricken at the sight of the poor creatures. She bemoaned the sin wrought upon them, mostly due to negligence. In the end, it didn't matter whether she could really take care of them all or not; she bought every one. Not long after, she made them all... what, for lack of a better description, might be called a set of clothes, sewn together out of old blankets, curtains, and whatever other bits of clothing she had to hand… all to cover their bare little bums… I guess… Since Mum was rather skilled with a needle and thread, it really wasn't all that difficult for her…

Not only did she make them clothes, she also knit underpants for the dog (a form of contraception, really), and brassieres for the cows (which helped wean the calves).

As the main purpose of the animal attire was to ward off mosquitoes and the winter cold, appearance wasn't really a consideration. Once clothed, well, let's just say the creatures' bare bottoms stayed clear of the ground, among other things.

Unsurprisingly, most of the animals reacted indignantly towards Mum's gift. They didn't seem to understand the clothes were for their benefit. Indeed, after we'd put them on, they responded as though we were trying to punish them for some indiscretion and began running wildly about, jumping and scratching as best they could at the clothes that then tightly wrapped around them. It was really quite a scene, especially when they spun themselves around and around, mistakenly believing, as it were, that this action would somehow relieve them of the layers they were wearing. After realising this approach would not work, the animals took to squeezing through the tightest places they could, notably the narrow cracks between the fences, vainly hoping, or so it seemed, to pull the clothes off in the process. Unfortunately for them, they had all underestimated Mum and her needle.

After a period of… adjustment… the animals all grew used to their new outfits. They also obtained new names. The chickens that wore red were now called as such. There were also green chickens… and an assortment of other colours. In the mornings, we'd open the compound and soon be swarmed by a rainbow of pecking mouths – red, yellow, blue, purple and so on. It was quite the magnificent display.

The other members of the work unit also began to refer to Mum differently, calling her leader of a beggars' union, a designation somewhat less flattering, even if it did perhaps fit. That is, her coterie of chickens, decked out as they were in their haphazard rags of multicoloured stitchings, were still an unkempt bunch, many lacking combs, many crippled, and many constantly rocking left and swaying right, missing claws or, in some cases, whole feet. Needless to say, wherever they roamed and wherever they ended up, they would always cause gasps of surprise and astonishment amongst the villagers whose eyes happened to fall upon them – at least at first. Afterwards, it was only the strangers who happened to be in town that paid the beggars' union any mind.

This was especially the case for the drivers of coaches who occasionally passed through. Upon seeing the eclectic legion of chickens scramble across the road in front of them, festooned in myriad colours, they couldn't help but slam on their brakes and bring their vehicles to a sudden, and in some cases violent, stop. After all, a scene such as this had to be given closer inspection, or so many of them thought.

While they might've been offensive to the more sensitive eye, the wardrobes did do the trick. The creatures no longer feared the mosquitoes during the day, nor did they fear the bitter cold at night. (Near the Gobi, the temperature change from morning to night was extreme.)

Two months later, the bare skin of the animals showed a noticeable improvement. Swelling had decreased, and it had even, to some degree, regained its normal hue. (It had been a purplish red before.) The many sores and blisters had also begun to heal and scab over. By spring, the wounded pores and hair follicles began to show signs of new growth as soft down could not only be seen but also felt. A year later, each chicken, aside from the tips of some of their stunted wings, were resplendent in new feathers. And I'm not talking just about tender new fuzz, but actual feathers, healthy and strong. I'm not really sure how Mum made it happen, but not a single chicken died in her care. It was really something, even if they were an ugly, motley crew of chicks; so hideous, in fact, that none of us dared eat them (which may have contributed in some measure to none having actually died).

To save on chicken feed, Mum, on numerous occasions, planned to slaughter some of the fowl. But when she stood above them, knife in hand, and saw their scarred and once wounded flesh, their malformed feet, their infirm combs... an unfeigned wave of nausea would rise up in her... and she was unable to let the knife fall... Thereafter, not a feather on their heads was hurt, and they all lived to a ripe old age. Mum saw to that.

They say that out of great tragedy, good fortune can arise... I guess this was an example of that... at least for the chickens. Naturally, of course, Mum's relationship with them meant that when she moved out to the countryside, they came with her. I guess they were used to swallowing life's bitterness, used to fighting for every inch. Life out in the wilderness couldn't have been that much more of a challenge, although it did perhaps toughen them up even more.

It's quite interesting then, to compare the second generation of chickens Mum brought from the town, for they were more akin to innocent, unspoiled young women, at least at first. A few days after being relocated out into the wilderness, these pure young women were wholly transformed, first into shrews, and then later into bandits. That is, when it came time to feeding, they acted more like vicious animals than relatively meek chickens. First, they'd encircle me menacingly, surrounding my position as though they were an army launching a siege. Then they'd start jumping and skittering about. Feathers would fly. I felt as though they'd swallow me if they had the chance. If they were people behaving in such a chaotic manner... well, needless to say, the incidence of people trampling on one another would be that much more severe.

In fact, there was one chicken that was particularly fierce. If my own skin was uncovered, even just a bit – say, for instance, my ankle – it would immediately target it for attack, and my own negligence would be keenly rebuked... I used to think only geese would bite a person with the same ferocity as a dog, but after this I was intensely aware of the pain a chicken's beak could cause. They certainly belied their name...

Heavens did it ever hurt!

I suppose it was more accurate to describe them as locusts, or some other such insect that would not let go of flesh once it had bitten into it. It's true, I would contort my leg every which way and shake it as violently as I could, but still the creature just wouldn't let go... damn monster!

I guess some of the mob really were those fighting chickens you sometimes hear about.

DUCKS

For a period of time while I lived in Akehala, I had no internet. Consequently, when situations arose, I'd have little choice but to ring my friend and bother (harass?) her for help. I remember I once telephoned her to ask how best to make salted duck.

"How the hell should I know? I've never made it before."

"Then get online and find out how."

"Why do you want to make it in the first place?"

"Because it's easy to store away and it lasts a long time."

"Just put the duck in the fridge..."

"I've got more than thirty – if I butcher them all they won't fit."

"Then don't kill 'em all at the same time, you idiot... kill 'em only as you need 'em."

"That won't work... I've gotta do it... at the same time. They eat too much... they're like bloody pigs... always stuffing their faces and quacking for more. I simply don't have enough food to give them."

"Why do you have so many anyways?"

"Because Mum wanted to make some down-filled jacket..."

"Eh... why didn't she just buy a jacket at the market... she didn't have to try and make her own..."

"You're right... I told her the same thing... but she's suspicious of everything at the market... She just doesn't believe they use actual duck down... The only person she trusts is herself... She also thinks she's good with a needle and thread... that there's nothing she can't sew."

As you can see, the ducks weren't my idea.

Raising ducks is no easy thing, nor is removing their feathers. The first time I did... well, that was when I understood why duck-down clothes are so much more expensive than things made out of cotton... it was so damn hard getting those feathers! How hard? I'm not sure how to put it... I reckon it can only be compared to, say, unravelling a cross-stitch... thread by thread. And not just any cross-stitch, I mean something properly magnificent, twenty metres long, a picture of ten thousand li of rivers and mountains, a facsimile of Zhao Fu's 'Ten Thousand Li of the Yangtze River' – something like that... I imagine doing the cross-stitch would be less of a hassle!

To pluck the feathers, you first need boiling water to massage and loosen the flesh. After that, you can start pulling them out. The most important thing, however, is to not damage the duck down, which means you can only grab them one at a time. It's best to pull the longest and hardest feathers first, and then continue layer by layer until the bird is dead and there's only one layer left... That's when you can take the last ones out.

I couldn't help but feel terrible at the end of it. Do you know the constitution of duck feathers? How they grow? What they're capable of? It's a fair deal more complicated than the most confounding of chemical experiments. They are more accurate and precise than the most advanced piece of technology. And how they link together... my word... they're more detailed than the most sophisticated of architectural blueprints... That's the skill of nature... we humans have nothing to compare to it.

At least... that's how it might've been in the past... Now we use nature's brilliance to make... clothes for us. Gosh, it was so bloody hard to remove those feathers...

By the time I got half a duck done, my hands would be aching, nearly ruined. After finishing thirty ducks... I was seriously reconsidering my daughterly feelings towards Mum. I was at a critical juncture, let me tell you. My own personal circumstances didn't help, I suppose. I was jobless, without an income, and had no place of my own to live.

There I was, sitting under a set of eaves, my head kept low.

Although I personally didn't think raising ducks for the purposes of making a duck-down jacket was especially sound, it wasn't my place to say anything, or rather, I didn't feel that I could intrude upon what Mum considered her domain of work. I just had to do what she told me to. True, there probably were other methods to pluck duck feathers, and I'm sure those engaged in the industrial processing of duck down had certain technology, but I didn't know anything about these supposed methods. For an isolated town in the middle of nowhere such as Akehala, if Mum wanted a duck down coat, then it was perhaps inevitable that a cockamamie method would have to be thought up. Like what the poor people did ages ago when they first came out into this wilderness. When they thought about getting a new article of clothing, well, I imagine it would take at least two years of lead-in time. That is, the cotton would first have to be picked, processed into thread, weaved into reams of cloth, and then transported over the mountains and grasslands to a dye factory. By the third year say... the new clothes would be ready to be worn.

Sometimes I wonder if we're really living in the twenty-first century...

Ah... I still have lingering fears – trauma, I tell you – about that experience... pulling out those bloody feathers...

That year I returned, Mum immediately put me in charge of the ducks. I was to be their 'commander'. She entrusted me with all of them, more than thirty, both big and small. Thereafter, I spent my days racing up and down the small river, my babouche-like slippers discarded on the riverbanks, a long stick in my hand... a military baton to keep my charges in order.

There's a certain romanticism associated with the term 'goose girl'. The Grimm Brothers' fairy tale has seen to that. But 'duck girl'... that just sounded strange, very strange. What's more, ducks were a lot more troublesome than geese. All they seemed to know how to do was quack, quack, quack repeatedly throughout the day. And there were thirty of them I had to look after... divided into two factions who spent as much time warring over territory as they did quacking. As the officer in charge, it was my job to stand in between them, to quell the hostilities, but I felt no sense of power to actually do it.

That first year I took care of them, the small river out behind the house was their peach blossom grove... their utopia. Most of them spent as much time as they could out there, whiling away the daylight hours frolicking in the water. When winter came and the land froze, the ducks retreated inside their enclosure to keep warm. They'd stay there, too, for the entire season. Once the spring thaw began, they would re-emerge, looking filthy and dishevelled as though each one had washed with nothing but an old, tattered mop for the better part of twenty-odd years. As soon as the ice broke, I hurriedly rounded up my charges and directed them all to the water. I thought that once they saw the gurgling stream now free of ice, they would happily dive into it. Who would've thought they'd stand on the riverbanks dumbfounded and unable to move? At best, there was one or two of them that edged towards the water, dipped their heads in, and then promptly pulled them back out. It looked very much like they were giving themselves a sponge bath. That was it.

A thought occurred to me as I watched them, I remember. Perhaps they'd forgotten the benefits the water had provided them and needed a few days to recall how much they'd enjoyed it in the past... Yes, time, I thought, was all they required... But time didn't work, it seemed, or rather they decided not to return to old habits... I don't know... But each and every duck soon became what could only be called a dry fowl, with at most a few of them running down to the water for a drink and nothing more.

I'd never seen... idiot ducks before. And in that moment, I decided to help them as best I could. My first thought was to get them back into the water – they were ducks, after all. To do that, I marched over to stand in front of them, knelt down and lifted one up in my arms. Then I flung it into the stream. I figured the creature would be terrified at first, but that it would also remember being in the water. As the saying goes, like a duck to water.

But I guessed wrong. What I saw... Gosh, the poor thing sank like a rock... I'm not exaggerating... It did... It just sank... I tell you, I'd never seen the like before!

Sink, sank, sunk... I was stunned. And then, just when I thought it was doomed, it managed to poke its head up out of the water, just a little. I couldn't believe it was struggling as much as it was. But despite all of its effort, the most it could do was keep its small head above water. And I do mean only its head – you couldn't see anything else, not even its neck, which was fortunate as its neck wasn't all that long! Luckily, it was also able to flap its wings under the surface of the water; this at least propelled it towards the banks. It was amazing to see it struggle so much, and pitiful, really, that a duck could only flop and push itself towards the edge, then half roll, half crawl up on the shore.

I realised something, though, as I watched. It wasn't that they'd forgotten how to swim, or that they'd somehow grown to distrust the water, it was that they understood only too well their own bodies, their weight, the distribution of body fat, what had happened to them over the winter, and how their bodies had changed.

I understood, too, that they hadn't rested at all during the winter. All they'd done was stuff their little faces!

Let's talk again about slaughtering the ducks. Mum was the executioner. Each time she let the blade fall, she would mouth to herself the following words: "Shed the wool sweater, put on the plain cotton one, shed the wool sweater, put on the plain cotton one..."

"Shed the wool sweater, put on a plain cotton one." This was... a kind of ceremonial mantra Granny used to say when she took a life. Such was the fate of livestock, I suppose. Perhaps after death took them they'd be reincarnated into the human world... I suppose you could consider this as words of consolation for the departed spirit of the animals, part of a religious ceremony that sent them off to the bardo to await reincarnation... I don't know. All I do know is that they'd been passed down to Mum as a sort of cultural heritage, a means to help her handle the bloody ritual of killing livestock, a means to assuage her heart at the death she meted out... If only a little.

Even after the massacre, Mum continued to sorrowfully chant: "Blood drips, drips everywhere, drips the day through..."

A long time ago, I remember it well... Mum hadn't been so concerned about slaughtering livestock. But then... something happened. I don't know what, I don't know how, but something had pulled her heartstrings, had made her incapable of taking a life, even that of a domesticated beast. And she stayed like this for ages, not daring to kill. If she did have need (which of course she did), she'd always get someone else to do it. Out in the countryside... well, that changed. Finding someone to butcher animals wasn't exactly the easiest thing to do... And so... when the need arose... she'd once more have to take the knife in her hand and kill. It became a sort of routine... She'd refuse, then be forced, however reluctantly, to go ahead with it, only to swear that was the last time... until she needed to do it again.

Finally, after many such iterations of this routine, Granny's words came back to her. They gave her a sense of... I don't know... moral rightness... perhaps... about killing livestock, and thus she regained her confidence with the butcher's blade... or, as was more likely, she realised she had, in some circumstances at least, no other option.

Ah... those ducks... thirty friggin' ducks... She slaughtered twenty-six, leaving four. When I saw their corpses piled high... I wanted to wretch... It was disgusting... I never ate duck after that... Couldn't even think about it.

As for the survivors, those four fortunate fowl, they lived for many years. Two even reached such an age that their bodies began to break down and they ended up mostly paralysed. Mum still took care of them though... I suppose it was a sort of... luck of the draw... I mean, if an animal survived its brush with death, then it was assured of a relaxing old age, guaranteed to be well fed and well cared for... right? Interesting that...

As for those ducks out in the sunflower fields, they were part of another brood. They weren't to be used for their down, either. No, their home was the irrigation canals that fed the fields.

It was all good, I guess. Mum was out here, in the wild, and she wasn't going to leave, so it made sense for her to use the resources she had to hand. I'll say one more thing, though. Raising ducks out here in the wilderness, well, the greatest reward is the quack, quack, quack – a duck's voice carried far, it was much ruder and more unreasonable, much louder and clearer... it resonated with a certain... vitality, a vigour for life. And in the wild, in that expanse of grassland and emptiness, the sudden ear-piercing shriek of a raft of ducks was a type of comfort, an inspiring cackle that urged us to keep at it, to keep going... strange as that may be.

25

RABBITS

The rabbits we had were like the dogs, always clinging to people, circling about them, and never going too far away, especially one particular one in the warren... it never ventured more than a hop or two away. Even when Mum went out into the fields to work, sometimes at quite a distance, this one rabbit would invariably tag along. Mum would discourage the creature, of course, urge it to turn around. She nearly always had farther to go, but the rabbit would simply spin its head around, look in each direction, and then refuse to follow her orders, or even to acknowledge her suggestion.

"But look at yourself," Mum would continue on. "You haven't a pair of shoes on your feet, and you've already come a rather long way... Surely your little feet must be hurting, hmm..."

The rabbit's ears would twitch calmly, seemingly unbothered by her words. Mum would set off again, and before she took more than a few steps, the rabbit would be hopping contentedly behind her. Independent. Full of life. Unmistakably proud. (One might even say haughty.) When the creature shut its small, reddish eyes, it was as though the world between heaven and earth had been shorn of its most precious pearls. Mum loved having the rabbit follow her, truth be told. She was grateful for its company. Its presence seemed to push aside, if only temporarily, all of the toil, strife and hardship of life out on the plains. There were even times when she couldn't help herself – she just had to mimic the rabbit's hop and experience the land from its unique perspective.

This single rabbit really was quite fond of Mum, but I couldn't really say why. Perhaps it was the loneliness between them, like the moon and the earth, tied together in this limitless galaxy until time itself stopped, one rabbit and one old lady, my mum, here in this corner of existence, at sea in a boundless sunflower field that rolled on and on. Who could abandon the other?

Saihu loved Mum, too. But her fondness was of a different order. Saihu loved the sense of security Mum brought. That's why she was always on the edge of panic – terror, really – that one day Mum might no longer be there, just as Granny had disappeared without warning.

Saihu also loved the rabbits. Not long after one of the first little critters was born, Mum, cupping the small infant kit in her hands, showed the creature to Saihu, who reacted as though she'd been shown something out of a dream world. She was slow and cautious around the tiny thing, initially confused as to what it was, before growing more comfortable and then leaning in to give it a tender kiss. This new life, or so it seemed, was soon no stranger to Saihu at all, but rather a part of herself. Her canine heart appeared to swell with love for the little animal Mum held in her hands. It was as though she was accepting responsibility for its fate. It was really rather touching, I must say.

It's in their nature for rabbits to dig holes. I used to wonder whether, if they were let loose out in the countryside like the chickens were, they would be able to establish their own warren, a rabbit kingdom under the ground... I worried about their numbers, too – about whether they would decline the more we cared for them. The opposite, in fact, happened. They flourished. This was due in large part to how well they were fed when Mum first moved out here – she'd mixed wheat husks and corn with leftover sunflower oil to make a delicious rabbit feast. Occasionally, she'd also give them a leaf or two of our own vegetables. When the dinner bell was rung, it wasn't only us racing back for our meals, but the rabbits, too. (I imagine, though, that they enjoyed the taste of what Mum had made more than we did.) It wasn't long before the females began having litters of kits, thus increasing their numbers many times over.

This, however, brought a new problem for Mum. She soon grew concerned that the larger warren would ultimately descend on the sunflower fields and devour the new sprouts before they had a chance to grow. That concern was something everyone could understand, if for no other reason than that the sunflowers were vital to our life out here... If they were suddenly and completely devoured, well, we could all forget about having better meals in the future.

From seedling to harvest, the life cycle of the sunflower plants was about three months. In those three months, the kits grew into rabbits and had broods of their own. Were the sunflowers as eternal as the rabbits seemed to be? For us, how could we think of the sunflowers in any other terms? What they produced in three months fed our futures, our destiny. Their magnificence was deeply entangled with our memories... everything was connected to them, our lives intimately bound to them and their continued existence.

I would stare out onto this simple and crude land, at the delicate dirt path that wound its way in front of our door, at the desert needlegrass that stood guard over it... and I would make a supreme effort to commit it all to memory, down to the smallest detail. It was as though I knew that at some point in the future, I'd reminisce and picture this scenery in my mind. It would be my avaricious attempt to recapture that moment, a form of greed to try and re-experience it again.

The rabbits, however, didn't care. They would lead me deep into the wilderness, hopping always ahead, looking around every three or five hops to make sure I was still tagging along. I thought I must keep the memory of these creatures in my mind, too. But as they bounded left to right, they would periodically disappear out of sight, subverting my chance to crystallise them in my memory... except, perhaps, for their eyes, which were always crimson and cold when they looked back at me.

In the dense sunflower fields, the rabbits were prone to losing their way, often not returning when the sun set. On such nights, Mum would toss and turn, before eventually throwing on her jacket and walking out into the night herself to shout into the fields: "Rabbits, rabbits! Raaaabbbbiiiittttssss!"

I remember it being especially dark one night – more so in amongst the sunflowers and the small stream that wound its way through it. Even the brightness of the rabbits' fur and eyes were swallowed up and absorbed by the darkness. I dreamed someone else was out there – a man... He reached down and embraced a rabbit tightly in his arm... He tried to steal it away... his head never once turning around to see if anyone had seen him... But then, at the sound of Mum's plea, the man hesitated... Then he walked through my dream and wakefulness came to me.

The following morning... the missing rabbit returned on its own, its fur spotless and white, its demeanour quiet and calm, everything seemingly new.

Day and night out here in this wild expanse were diametrically opposed. The shimmering sunflower fields appeared to be light years away from the darkness of the night. Only the rabbits traversed this barrier between the setting of the sun and the rising of the moon. Theirs was the only path unimpeded. When the sun was up, the rabbits would stay close by, but as soon as it set, they'd disappear before we could take a second look. Standing at the mouth of this door between two worlds, I recall feeling dismayed and dejected at the size of my physical body, my inability to follow after them, the heaviness of my heart and my world.

We decided then that we had to leave this place. Mum took down the yurt, as well as the iron-plated chimneys she had constructed. She flung the latter out into the emptiness. The rabbits didn't understand what was happening, and they stood, to a soul, confused and bewildered, faced suddenly with some new game of life. The chimneys were to be caves as they quickly scurried through them, oblivious to what we were doing. In an instant, white rabbits were transformed into a charcoally warren... They seemed to be so unconcerned about their once splendidly white fur!

There was an older one, its arse rather large, who got wedged inside one of the chimney tubes. It had no clue how it had got itself so spectacularly stuck, and it took to whining repeatedly to be set free.

I didn't realise they could make such a sound! I'd always thought the rabbits were mute.

Mum stood still as soon as she heard the poor creature's wail. Then she laughed heartily... and loud. A second later, she was shouting for us to pick the chimney up and stand it on its end. Then she banged on it for what seemed to be nearly half a day before the heavy-set rabbit scampered free.

26

THE VILLAGE

I knew this move wouldn't be easy, that it'd be much more of a nuisance – we had chickens, ducks, rabbits and two dogs to transport. But on the morning of the move, Mum sent me off first, excusing me from the laborious work that had to be done. I was off the hook. In fact, in a nearby village, just on the other side of a field of sunflowers, Mum had found a small place where I could stay over. It was a single-room structure made of mud bricks, the first of its kind in the town.

We rode her motorcycle to get there. After we arrived, she pulled out a set of very old keys attached to a nearly worn-through piece of rope and unlocked the door. There wasn't much inside – only an old- and tired-looking bed made of rough wood, and a brick oven that didn't appear to be entirely trustworthy. The windows had frames, but no glass; only ripped and tattered plastic bags served as a barrier to the wind and sand. There was no ceiling either – nothing but the rough-hewn wooden beams haphazardly placed atop the four walls. Given the condition of the structure and its lack of protection from the elements, I didn't really understand why the door had been locked. I was more surprised still when I glanced at the back of the door, for there was no bolt, or anything else for that matter, and so no way to lock the door from the inside.

I wondered what Mum would do when night came. I suppose a stick or something else could've been wedged behind the door at night, but this would work only if the door swung inwards. It didn't. Mum's solution to this problem was... unique: once we were both inside, she picked up a hammer and nails and sealed the door tight. Then she tied a piece of rope around her hand, before notching the other end of the rope around the door handle. This was how I was supposed to close and secure the door at night. Mum explained it several times, then removed the nails, climbed back on her bike and left. My eyes watched as her figure disappeared over the horizon.

I'd seen Mum off, and now I was left alone in this... place. I plopped down on the bed and did nothing. Or rather I didn't know what to do. I'm not sure how much time passed, but finally I decided I might as well open up my luggage and at least make the bed I had little choice but to sleep on. I thought about cleaning up, perhaps mopping the floor, but I had no mop to actually try. Besides, the floor was nothing but earth, and there really wasn't much that could be done with it anyway. I mean, the room didn't even have cheap bricks for a floor, just the ground itself. There was nothing on the walls, either – no lime plaster, which was customary on adobe walls. No, they were just moulded earth and wheat husks, mixed together and then erected into the structure I was in. No effort had been made to disguise the coarseness of their providence.

Wait, that's not wholly true. There was something on the walls, but I'd rather it hadn't been there. Right in front of where the bed was positioned, someone had written a line not particularly comforting. In big, red and rather offensive calligraphy, two sentences were scrawled across the mud wall. The first one read: *All death wants love.* The second one read: *Please don't hurt me again.* I guessed the previous tenants had been Han Chinese. And by the looks of it, I was sure it was some young and lonely boy... maybe a girl... but more than likely a boy.

The village, however, was predominately Kazakh. Built deep in the wilderness, it was terribly remote, isolated and quiet. The kind of person who ended up in a place like this, renting a shack like this, I figured it had to be a migrant worker… someone dragged out here by his boss… probably with the promise of some big construction project or other. Either that or people like… me and Mum.

Later on, I don't know what time it was for it didn't seem to exist here, I crawled under my quilt, nestled in for the night and stared at those words until I finally fell asleep. My sleep was fitful, and I kept waking up throughout the night. And then, before I knew it, the sun was coming up and I couldn't help but feel tired and dazed. I imagine everyone else who'd slept in the bed experienced the same kind of night – tossing and turning until morning forced its way in.

The following day, I took a stroll through the town. I locked the door once I stepped outside, just as Mum had done, even if it wasn't really needed. There were about the same number of people in the village as there were on the upper and lower reaches of the Ulungur. Most were engaged in shepherding. Since it was summer, the majority of the livestock and all of the able-bodied men were deep in the northern mountains with their herds, leaving only one or two people at home to watch over the small plots of land used to produce fodder for the animals. Unsurprisingly, the town was quiet, almost deathly so.

According to state regulations, besides the small bit of land used for growing fodder, each household was also given a dozen or so acres to seed crops for personal use. Since no herdsmen were especially expert at farming, however, nearly all of them had rented their land to outsiders, which is how we got the fields we had.

Quiet and empty. I walked from one end of the town to the other, and the only people I saw were two men sat outside the only small shop in the village. It was easy to see they were the town's local drunks, sat in the shade on a wooden bench, glass in hand and barely a word exchanged between them. Around their feet lay their most recent conquest: a dozen or so empty bottles of beer. My arrival, however, caused a temporary halt to their libations. Instead of focusing on the glasses in their hands, they directed their attention towards me, trying to ascertain just who in hell I was and what in hell I was doing in their wasted – quite literally – little town. The door into the store was oddly narrow and misshapen. The windows were equally strange, short and small and encased in frames painted a motley green colour. The adobe walls had seen far too many seasons, and insects had bored far too many holes at their base. It was clear the building was sinking into the ground, if for no other reason than when I peered inside I noticed the steps were angled down into what was a sort of shallow pit that served as the shop's floor. I hesitated a moment, before pushing the ramshackle door open.

The store was pitch-black, and it took a few seconds before my eyes could adjust. There was a wooden counter at the far end as well as wooden shelves on either wall. But there were very few items. Suddenly, however, my eyes were drawn to a jar of osmanthus hair oil, a rather strange – and old – thing to find out here. I shifted my eyes to scan the other products on the shelves, lingering here and there, but ultimately I didn't buy anything.

That evening, Mum came to collect me. I rolled up the quilt and the few other belongings I had and attached them to the rear of the bike. Then I turned and locked the door behind me. It was strange. In that moment when I bolted the door, the familiar melancholy felt many times before when I left some place welled up inside me again. I'd only stayed in the... I can't call it a room... the shack... whatever... I stayed between the four walls but one night, spent only half a day in that small village, but somehow there was a sense of familiarity about it, and now I was sad to leave. Very bizarre.

A NEW HOME

We left the small village, and Mum angled the motorbike north, speeding across the earthen road and kicking up no small amounts of dust in our wake. We rode for what seemed like forever until finally we crested a ridge, and the landscape in front of us was transformed into a shimmering expanse of watery blue. We both gasped in surprise at the sight. We never dreamed such a place could exist out here. The image of that great wide expanse of water stunned us so thoroughly that we were at a loss for words. And at the same time, it dawned on us how choked with dust and earth our previous home had been.

We'd reached the great reservoir.

As we drove over the large dam and met the wind that came blowing over the body of water, things seemed fresh and new. Then we turned west towards a large swathe of reeds and quickly saw the hydroelectric plant nestled in the shade of lush, green trees. Mechanical rooms and worker dormitories were just beyond it. The former were closest to the sluice gates, and just below them the waters ran violently, a veritable waterfall that bubbled and churned, flowing east to west. On the opposite side of the river, the desert stretched far into the horizon. The sand gleamed in stark contrast to the water – pure, clean, desolate. As the sun set, the desert was bathed in a golden hue, transforming it into something grand and magnificent. On our side, there was the long, slender strip of vegetation. The southern reaches were our sunflower fields. There were also towering Lombardy poplars and alongside them shorter, but equally verdant, jujube trees.

Mum halted the bike on the eastern edge of the forest, got down and proceeded to walk in amongst the trees. Finally, in an open space fairly close to the dormitories, she stamped down the vegetation and claimed: "Here's where we'll set up our new home." In that moment, a great feeling of elation exploded throughout me. I couldn't say why.

Then we waited – all through the day and into the night – for the moving truck that was late. We tried ringing Uncle, but the service was poor and we couldn't make a good connection. We thus had no way to reach the driver. Our anxiety grew the longer we waited, especially as it was getting later and later, and this was no place to spend the night in the dark. We were also growing increasingly worried that the driver may have got into an accident, or that something else had happened. The night marched on, stars became visible in the sky above us, and our worries grew. As did the silence between us. Our eyes were drawn to the southeast, to the enveloping darkness that stretched into infinity.

Like the night, time marched on too, drawing it along with us, increasing our perturbation, until suddenly a sharp beam of light appeared in the distance. It grew steadier and steadier, snaking its way along the dirt road we ourselves had travelled, growing ever brighter as it drew closer. Gradually, we heard the sound of the truck as well. The driver had finally arrived, and we could start to feel a little more at ease.

There was no moon, and even though there were many stars in the night sky, you still couldn't see your hand in front of your face. We ended up unloading the truck as quickly as we could using our mobile phones as torches. While we did so, the driver argued vehemently with Uncle… about what we didn't know. Meanwhile, Mum muttered to herself, complaining that this had been lost, that had fallen out, and so on. The more I listened, the more I felt exhausted, the more I grew apprehensive. I worked robotically alongside them, unloading pile after pile of stuff. The hope I'd felt earlier in the day, the joy and enthusiasm for the future, had in a moment completely vanished, retreated to the nether reaches of my mind.

Then the wind picked up. Strange sounds rang out from all sides, and the temperature dropped. I thought to myself I ought to find my quilt, the one I'd used the night before in that small Kazakh town. But how could I? There was nothing but a pile of household items lying on the ground in the dark. It was a complete mess with things all over the place, some even broken, and all without form in the night. Mum continued to complain, and I could tell she was getting angrier and angrier. The driver then tossed out the last bundle of stuff, climbed up into his cab, slammed the door and left. No words were exchanged.

In the vehicle's absence, the wind grew stronger. The area grew darker and emptier. We grew even more silent. The light from our mobile phones weakened. Our future home was just that – in the future. It could only protect us in the future. At that moment, we had no roof over our head, only a disordered mess strewn about the ground. All of the hardship, all of the pain of this itinerant life trapped us in that moment and prevented us from escaping.

28

AN UNFAMILIAR PLACE

Mum had chosen this spot near the dormitories housing the workers who toiled in the hydro plant because it was, on first inspection, flat and dry – an ideal place for her yurt. She'd also selected this spot for its closeness to other people, the proximity to a work unit helping to set her heart at ease. But while this location made Mum feel better, the cadres only felt miserable at the arrival of their new neighbours. Don't forget, we brought our animals with us, notably our shoe-thieving dog Chouchou... who now found himself suddenly amongst many, many more feet, and many, many more pairs of shoes. Needless to say, he was overjoyed and almost immediately put his unique... skill... to work. Before a week had past... we'd ended up falling foul of every worker at the plant.

The work at the hydroelectric station was done in shifts, which meant the teams tending the station switched every two weeks. I suppose this arrangement made sense – after all, living and working out here in this desolate, quiet place, year after year, took quite a toll on most people. In fact, most couldn't handle it. As a result, when the shifts changed every two weeks, those coming off duty couldn't help but be ecstatic; they were free, if only for a short time, which meant they quickly washed their shoes, put them out to dry, then cleaned themselves up before finally racing off back to the city. Not one of them would glance back, either. Not one of them missed the drudgery of their work.

Of course, after we arrived, or rather after Chouchou arrived, many of the men would end up not being able to find their shoes. It didn't take long for them to guess who the culprit was, but what could they do – they didn't have all that much time, and returning to the city had to take precedence.

Unfortunately for them... and for us, too, I suppose, it didn't take Chouchou long to escalate his attacks and start targeting their slippers, leaving them with nothing to put on their feet whatsoever. And surely they couldn't head back into the city without shoes, could they? No, they had to find the thief, and that eventually led them to us.

Now, it's true, if it hadn't been for one of the workers actually witnessing Chouchou committing the crime, in all likelihood they never would've cracked the case. But since someone had seen him, it wasn't long before they all gathered together to hunt for the shoe-thieving animal.

I'm not sure how many kilometres they ended up traversing, but however many there were, they weren't successful in apprehending Chouchou – at least not at first. But as they say, a monk can run away, but the temple won't follow, meaning that sooner or later, the men were bound to locate poor Chouchou. Ultimately, the workers surrounded our yurt and began hurling complaints at Mum. "That damn mutt just latches onto our shoes and runs! He runs fuckin' fast, too! Even dodges stones thrown at him... and he won't release our damn shoes, either!"

Mum and I were both alarmed at these developments and terribly angry. We had to get Chouchou to return his stolen footwear and stop doing it altogether.

"Chouchou!" hollered Mum in all directions. "I've got something tasty for you!" And wouldn't you know it... in an instant he appeared.

The only problem was he'd returned without a single shoe in his mouth. We had no way to question him, and besides, he wouldn't tell us if he could. All we could do was head out into the wilderness to search for the missing shoes ourselves. We found some, but not others. The shoes weren't the only thing that had been lost, for we lost much face due to the fiasco.

"I'm really sorry to say this... I really, really am..." The embarrassment in Mum's voice was unmistakable. "But in future you'll need to look after your shoes... and certainly don't leave them out in the open where Chouchou..."

"And *you* make sure to watch after that bloody dog!" They didn't let Mum finish.

She knew we were in the wrong in any case. Chouchou was our responsibility, which is why she apologised in the first place. Of course, she had to scold her dog, too.

Once the mob had departed, Mum turned to me to complain: "But how in hell are we gonna keep that beast under control? Tell me, should we invite them over here to handle the mutt?"

Then she searched around to find some meat to give to that stupid dog. After all, she got him to come home with the promise of something tasty, so she couldn't go back on her word. If she did, she wouldn't be able to trick him again in the future. In the end, Chouchou was let off, despite his crime, and there was nothing more to be said about it.

Although this was a lonely and secluded place, compared to the wilds in the south where we'd been before, this was a much more lively location, perhaps due to its proximity to the provincial highway and the Ulungur. There were about three or four villages nearby; well, sort of nearby – the nearest was about three kilometres away. I'm not saying we were inundated with guests. The road to the reservoir was a dead end after all, and aside from the livestock that would roam about irrespective of traffic rules, no one really had any free time, or any inclination, to explore or foolishly wander about the area given its remoteness. But it was nonetheless livelier than where we'd been.

Saihu soon became... popular... amongst the town's other dogs. I suppose it was a pity nothing ever came of such... relations.

As for Mum, she seemed to be more miserable than ever before. We'd come to what was a flourishing place, but all she felt was a sudden intensification of her own sense of insecurity. For days on end, she kept harping on about the past, as well as worrying about thieves and bandits. This was rather ironic, really, for she ought to understand better than anyone that we were all too bloody poor for thieves and bandits to even bother with. What's more, you'd've been hard pressed to find any unsavoury characters about as most of the inhabitants of the area were quite decent people. This was often the case, after all, in sparsely populated and incredibly isolated areas – everyone sort of knew they all had to pull together, and honesty and sincerity went much farther in a place like this than the opposite.

On that first evening we were there, we slept under the sky, facing the wind and the stars above, and feeling terribly exhausted at the same time. And like before, I tossed and turned the entire night, plagued by dreams and worries about this next chapter of our lives. I suppose our plight came across as rather dire to the reservoir workers, for on the following day, not long after the sun had crested the horizon, they showed up in droves to help us erect the yurt so that we wouldn't have to spend another night out in the open. Our yurt was up before we knew it, such was the effectiveness of their help, and a few hours later, once everything inside was set up, we could call it home. Mum was quite gratified and pleased by their assistance, and hopeful, too, that the future would be one of harmonious camaraderie with our new neighbours. Or something along those lines.

It's possible that would've been the case, too, if it weren't for Chouchou's actions and the stain it left on our reputation.

I didn't really know what the hydro plant actually did – at least not specifically – nor what the men and women working there were responsible for, for to my eyes they all seemed to have a great deal of leisure time. But whatever they did, they were all incredibly friendly and polite. Maybe that was because they'd seen the conditions we lived in; they did, after all, help with putting up the yurt and saw first-hand its rather rudimentary, no-frills state. Maybe that instilled in them a degree of sympathy... maybe.

There was, especially, one female worker who continually came round just to hang out and chat. She'd always bring deep-fried dough cakes with her, too, or steamed buns. At any rate, the food she brought wasn't what we normally ate, so...

Three days after we'd moved there, the director in charge of the hydro plant came by to tell us there was a vacant room on the southern side of the dormitory and that he would allow us to use it rent-free if we wanted to. At first, we were only too happy to say yes!

By the middle of autumn, the temperature was becoming noticeably colder. The days were still fine, that's true, but the nights saw the mercury plummet so much that two quilts were barely enough. The frigid nights also meant it was increasingly difficult to get out of bed in the mornings, and while our yurt did block some of the wind, it wasn't much better than a flimsy sail at warding off the elements. When a room was offered, well, how could we say no?

My enthusiasm at the prospect of having four walls, however, made the director feel a little uneasy about what he was offering. "Now... you know... Well, it's possible... Maybe you should go and see it first?"

We did as he suggested, and once I saw it, I knew what he'd been getting at. The place had been empty for years, and even though the doors and windows had been shut, during the winters they'd let the nearby farmers house their cattle inside, to protect them from the cold. As a result, the mud floor was covered in a thick layer of cow shit.

I was determined nevertheless, and returned to our yurt to grab a spade to start clearing out the filth from the room. After two hours of tiresome work though I gave up... For every layer I shov-elled out, there was another underneath. Shit, shit and more shit... I guess I overestimated my own determination to have the room – the four walls – instead of the yurt.

In the hallway running off from the room, the other dorm inhabitants couldn't help but peek in to see what I was doing, the curiosity in their eyes as plain as day. An hour later, the same people would walk by again. The expression on their faces had changed, however. Sympathy at my plight was what I saw then. I was sweating from head to toe, and every part of me was covered in grime. I was not only growing more and more exhausted but also feeling increasingly lonely. I stuck the shovel in again and again, and as I did so, thoughts wormed their way through my mind. This room would never be mine, could never be, and that's why it was putting up the struggle it was, challenging me with its dirt, resisting my efforts to make it clean and liveable. Suddenly, in that moment, I was the least envied person in the world, at least I felt this way... No one wanted to be where I was, not the workers at the hydro plant, nor the drunks in that sad little village, nor even the seasonal workers who had joined us for harvests in the past... no one. Their lives were infinitely more orderly than mine. There was a rhythm to their existence, a certain sort of calmness and comfort of the known. In their eyes, they could only look at me and wonder how it was that I was still there.

Wearing glasses and the same dirty work clothes day in and day out, trying to do the impossible, refusing to give up, obstinate, stubborn, but weak and frail at the same time.

What could I do but give up?

The cold was the cold.

I lifted up the spade and returned... home. As I walked closer, I could see it... our yurt was there... waiting for me... as it had always done.

29

GUESTS

A few days after we arrived, the yurt appeared as though it belonged to this place, as though it had been there for hundreds of years, if not more. Our first visitor was a drunk. We didn't know where he'd come from, nor why he came. Wait a minute, that's not right. To us, as outsiders, we assumed he had an ulterior motive. Why else would he visit? For the locals, however, his showing up at the door was nothing out of the ordinary. To drop in on someone, to eat and drink, to stay the night, that was all as it should be, regardless of whether or not a visitor had something on their mind or not.

Whatever his motives, he was a drunk of certain standards and maintained a degree of decorum, even on those occasions when he was completely inebriated. Thus, on his way to see us and not wanting to come empty-handed, he pilfered a few not-quite-ripened tomatoes that grew in a vegetable plot adjacent to the hydro plant. They were to be a gift for us, it seemed, and I remember him trying, ever so respectfully, to place them in my hands. I had to maintain my own decorum as well, which meant I had to graciously refuse his present, to demure and say there was no need, that he was being too polite, but in the end I would accept them – they were, after all, only a few tomatoes. My plan was to say no thanks three times and then accept.

Unfortunately, things did not go to plan, for after I refused the first time, he became greatly annoyed and, to be frank, noticeably pissed off. He began to shout, to accuse me of looking down on him. The odour of booze hung in the air. His sincerity was evident, and so the social etiquette that expected me to decline three times was wholly unnecessary. Useless even. What could I do but accept his gift and invite him in, offer him a seat at the small table that lay in front of the bed, and quickly prepare the tea?

We only had fresh tea – no milk. And besides a few biscuits, we had nothing else to offer to go along with it. Thankfully, he took no offence.

No one else was home, only me and the uninvited guest. We sat facing each other, neither of us saying anything. In that silence, we polished off two bowls of tea, and then he asked for something stronger. I knew this was how it was going to be! I knew he'd want alcohol. I was alone, and couldn't help but suspect his reasons for coming – how could I not? I thought it over for a second or two, even though there wasn't really anything to think about. I of course offered my apologies and refused his entreaties for drink.

"I'm sorry but... but... no one drinks in my family." My explanation was sincere, at least I believed it to be, so I volunteered additional details. "My uncle has high blood pressure, Mum's heart isn't too good..."

But before I could finish, I absentmindedly extended my leg and it brought up against something wedged in under the bed. Needless to say, I was taken aback and greatly surprised. I tried to hide what it was I'd discovered, but it was too late – he bent over curiously and reached out for what I had struck.

"What's this hey?... What? Eh! A bottle of wine!"

Mum had hidden it...

It'd been her habit to take a few nips after dinner, a nightcap as it were. It was how she enjoyed the end of the day. After winter, she'd've gone through about twenty-five litres of sorghum wine. Yeah, that was about right. I remember... usually before winter she'd buy those twenty-five litres, and since it was nearly spring, it made sense for this to be all that was left.

And now I could see the drunkard's eyes light up in anticipation. He forgave me my lie, even though I didn't realise it was such when I first spoke – either that or he was never offended by it in the first place, or maybe he'd never been lied to before... Perhaps he couldn't differentiate truth from falsehood...

Then I realised he'd probably heard these excuses before and had long since ceased to care. Either way, this last bit of alcohol in this last bottle of Mum's stash was the source of his rejoicing... so what was I to do?

He drained the remaining alcohol and then regaled me with stories of this and that, odds and ends, stories upon stories for hours and hours.

And then he stopped, stood up, and offered his goodbyes.

I heaved a sigh of relief, and then he suddenly leaned forward a little, apologised and told me he might've drunk too much. A moment later, he wobbled some more and then, regardless of possible consequences, he collapsed onto the bed and passed out.

What the hell was I to do?

Nothing, I suppose, except close the door and leave the poor sod where he was to sleep off the booze.

Two hours later when I returned, the man was gone. Then I heard it in the wind. If I listened closely, to the north, in the forest that grew there, I could hear someone singing, alone, his tune carrying in the air.

When there were lots of people about (although I must admit, there'd been only about a dozen hydro plant workers who'd come to visit), our old, rather flimsy yurt felt cramped and confined. At least to me it did. And no matter which way I craned my neck, things just wouldn't feel right.

And yet, our neighbours were a kind-hearted bunch. They looked upon our wretched and simple yurt with a modicum of benevolent concern, which, in turn, encouraged them to visit, to walk right in as though we were well-known members of the neighbourhood. What I was especially grateful for was... that people came to visit, whether they were old drunks or someone else. I grew especially fond of the hydro station director, who first came around during the Mid-Autumn Festival. His reason for visiting was to actually invite us to join them for lunch in the communal canteen. It was the harvest season, after all, and that meant they'd been given a little bit of a bonus which they'd splurged on the food. There would even be a great boiled chicken as the main course, he told us.

"We're all neighbours, aren't we?" proclaimed the director excitedly. "It only makes sense for us to enjoy the festivities together!"

While I did appreciate the gesture – how could I not – Mum and Uncle were still out in the fields busy at work, and I was the only one home. I didn't feel like going on my own – they were all strangers, really, and it was a holiday, which meant I'd feel even more out of place. There was nothing I could do, I thought, but refuse ever so politely.

That evening, when Mum and Uncle were back, we had our own meal and celebrated the moon harvest. We also invited the director to come around and enjoy the meal with us.

He was Kazakh, born during the Cultural Revolution. It was because of that he'd been given the name 'Revolutionary'. Well, his full name was 'Revolutionary Bekmуhamet', the second part being a common suffix given to Kazakh males. He'd become a Party member and a local cadre, so his spoken Chinese was excellent. This allowed us to chat the evening through, both guest and hosts. He told us about the area, how the people had many centuries ago surrendered to Genghis Khan's advancing hordes. After they'd yielded, they'd all had their arses branded with hot irons to mark their defeat, and to signal their new status as soldier-slaves in the Khan's army. Till today, he said, the trace of that branding... the stamp... was still visible on many local inhabitants.

Of course, that last bit was a joke. What wasn't a joke, however, was the fact that the locals had later on handed over control of their land to Genghis Khan's eighth son. I had no clue who the eighth son was, but I couldn't help but feel the weight of all of that history on their shoulders, the marks the past left on people many generations later. It's true that history becomes story, and that that stamp he spoke of was perhaps more fiction than anything else, but it didn't matter – the history that was told, generation after generation, had a tenacity and spirit not easy to destroy, especially when they are stories of tragedy or happiness.

From what I had been told, when Kazakh children were still very young, the most important thing they learned, what they had to study and commit to memory, was the names of all their ancestors going back nine generations. They also had to learn about and remember their specific family history, the ins and outs of it, its roots, and how they stretched from the past into the present. For Kazakhs, whether they lived in the smallest of small peasant villages, dirt poor and honest, or they were sunburned shepherds out in the fields, wearing the most tattered, the most frayed clothing imaginable, for each and every one of them there was an indelible chain following behind them, linking them to their ancestors, who in turn supported their descendants, helped them in their lives, kept the lines moving ever forward. That was what they learned as children.

That wasn't the case for us. Not anymore. We Chinese have given up on recording family histories. We don't know anymore where our families come from, what difficulties they fled. We don't appreciate the fact we are descendants of those who fled war and destruction, fled disaster. I didn't even know the names of my grandfathers. When one is careless and unconcerned about the past, one can't help but live carelessly, slovenly, without purpose. The yurt reflected this, and on those occasions when visitors came, they could see this too, and I'd see it on their faces in turn. Our relationships were always slapdash and chaotic, which helped to explain why no one ever came twice, I suppose. This general haphazardness carried over into the work in the fields, to everything. We were constantly out of step with the world, afraid to take the next step, yet unaware of what was actually over the horizon. I imagine a sober drunk knew much more of their place in the grand scheme of things than I did.

THE STOVE

When we lived further south, coal and liquid gas were our primary sources of fuel. But by the time we moved up near the reservoir, there wasn't all that much coal left, and the cylinder of gas was less than half full, with very little opportunity for us to refill it. Fortunately, however, the lushness of the area surrounding the water meant there was an abundance of vegetation, and thus dried wood, which could be used to light the cooking fires, and to save us a fair bit of cash, too. The only drawback was that this became my responsibility and part of my daily chores.

I couldn't say what kind of image I projected while out gathering firewood. All I could say was that I was a topic of interest for the hydro station workers, for they would often direct their attention and let it linger while I tromped through the woods collecting whatever dried bits – a twig, a branch – I could. Perhaps it was because I did the work alone... I just can't say. I never had to go very far out into the trees, but I wasn't all that close either... it was just bloody hard work.

I would notice the men looking at me, and I would wonder if I should wave, or call out a greeting while they were still some distance away. Or I could ignore them completely... until they drew closer and then it would be difficult *not* to notice them. On those occasions, it was best to stop what I was doing and instead direct my attention at them, then wait for them to look away as opposed to me averting my gaze.

I always bundled up in as many layers as I could when I was out in the woods working. I even had a kerchief to wrap around my head. The water coming off the river was always something to reckon with – it was cold and strong, and I was oh so afraid of the cold... I was also fearful of eyes spending too much time looking at me, sizing me up...

I'd been to the dorm and the canteen. They were plain and simple, very clean and tidy, so much so that you could imagine a great many years of honest work had been carried out there. I suppose I couldn't help but be a little jealous of it. No more so than when I was out collecting firewood. I remember thinking as I bent down to roll the sticks and twigs together in a bundle, as I lifted them up from the ground, usually getting dirty in the process, that this life, this disorganised existence I endured, had to be but temporary. It had to. But then I thought some more and realised my life had always been like this... my 'temporary' life had ended up becoming my whole life.

These thoughts would stay with me as I returned with the firewood, as I dropped it outside our yurt and then strolled around it. It was a mess, everywhere a mess, shit strewn all about the door, chickens skittering this way and that way. I kept walking, taking mental measurements as I did, wondering where we could construct a fence, where we could put the gate, and where a path could be beaten down that would take us to the river. I made plans – if we were going to be here for long – about how we could bring some order to this mess, how we could run things...

But the next month we left. And there was nothing to do but pack things up, clean up the area we essentially squatted on, and... pile up the firewood to be taken with us. I suppose that made this time a little different... In the past, we'd have just thrown the firewood away... Now we'd bundled it up neatly... until it was dinner time and then it was a mess of wood once more... at least until we used the whole lot.

For some reason, I clearly remember that pile of wood, how tidy it was. I remember taking it down with the rest of our stuff. Dinner had to be made... I took a few steps, stopped for a couple of seconds... and just stood there... admiring it... I don't know why... Then I lifted my feet and continued on, stooped inside, and set about lighting the cooking fire...

Burning wood was cheaper than burning coal. This was true. But the latter was much more convenient. You always had to keep your eye on the wood, making sure it was continually fed. There was also a great deal more smoke from a wood fire. If the stove wasn't managed properly, tears and runny noses would accompany every meal. There was also much more ash to deal with after the cooking was done. Usually with coal, I'd have to empty the tray once a day, but with wood it was at least three times as the ash would just pile up. I know that doesn't really sound like much, especially not for an active person like... say... Mum... but for a lazy arse like me it was a fuckin' nuisance. That said, and regardless of whether I'd used coal or wood, I was fond of the stove.

Now in comparison... yes, cooking with gas was the easiest... but there was no way I could enjoy it. I know, I know... its convenience is something to marvel at – one twist and the gas is on, another twist and it's off. That's really quite amazing. And it's true I'd spent a long time away from lighting fires – I'd been in the city for years, and I'd come to rely on the modern conveniences, the heaters and the gas ranges. But I still liked cooking over a fire – a proper fire – best.

Memories come rushing back. It's the middle of winter, cold and dark, so freezing in fact that the cold rips me from my sleep. The fire's been out for some time, and the frigidness of the air weighs down on everything as though it were some solid mass pressing down on us from outside. Wrapping my quilt around me, I step down from my bed, walk to the stove and open the hatch. A few weak embers remain, struggling mightily to stay warm against the biting cold. I pick up the poker and stab at the last bits of the fire, sifting carefully through the ash. I then grab a few pieces of coal – small, broken pieces to place on the embers. I open the flute on the bottom to let more oxygen in. The flames rise quickly, twirling up from the smouldering embers to embrace the bits of coal. It doesn't take long for the fire to grow, to dance phantom-like in the belly of the stove. The flames dance slowly at first, then become more and more vibrant. And as they do this, I can feel the warmth grow stronger and stronger...

Transfixed by the fire as it twisted and twirled inside the stove, I could feel my own internal brightness welling up.

In the north, in the dead of winter, in the middle of the night, the stove was the heart of any home. It was the main source of warmth, and its steadfastness had to be supported, its fire never allowed to go out. In the night with the stove burning, one could sit down to read in relative comfort while steamed buns roasted on top. From time to time, you would reach over to flip the buns until they gradually acquired a golden hue. Then you knew they were ready. You would lift them off the stove, toss them from hand to hand – they would be so hot – before finally pulling them apart to reveal the steamed, white softness inside. The night would be dark, just as the coal was. Dark shadows would also play amongst the roof beams. Impenetrable, formidable. But in the palm of your hand, you would hold such pure whiteness, a guard against the encroaching darkness. Its tender aroma would waft up around you and seal you off from the coldness in the air.

I prepared dinner by myself. I kneaded the dough, rolled it out and fried pancakes. I knew the power in my hands was incapable of changing the world, but it might be just enough to keep me and my family alive, just enough to transform what came from the earth into food in our bellies. The pancakes done, I boiled the kettle. Afterwards, I put out the flame, closed the stove, and waited for everyone to come home to eat.

31

QUIET

There was one particular spectacle out on the grasslands that lay just beyond the hydro station, and that was the number of wild rabbits running amok across the fields. Needless to say, Saihu and Chouchou had been kept incredibly busy after we moved here. They would spend most of their days trying to ambush the raging rabbits, with little success I might add, even if that didn't diminish their excitement.

When they withdrew from the battlefield, they would pant like mad and then dive their snouts into their water bowls and slurp even more frantically. After that, they'd stick close to me, or Mum, still snorting and heaving as they tried to regain their strength. It also appeared as though they were keen to drag either of us, or perhaps both of us, into their prolonged battle with the wild rabbits.

There were really rabbits everywhere. They'd whoosh and bound past you in the blink of an eye, sometimes so fast that all you'd hear was the rapid *thump thump* on the ground before they were gone. They were as quick as the wind, and the only thing you really ever saw was their shadow as it skittered by.

What impression did this give to us? Did it suggest the land was alive, vital and strong? Did it convey a sense of chaos, confusion and clamour? No, quite the opposite in fact, for the land seemed ever so silent. Indeed, I don't know what other animal could've been as quiet as those wild rabbits.

Although the wilderness was generally quiet, it took the appearance of the rabbits before you would become acutely aware of how quiet it really was. It was a sereneness that seemed more illusory than anything else – a type of nothingness, nothing but the wind and the grass, a rippling expanse that gifted a sense of kindness, the drifting clouds, thoughts dim and hazy.

The instant the rabbits appeared, all of this nature awoke, the horizon suddenly shrank, and the air grew taut, ever so slightly. My heart followed suit, and so did my ears. My throat was empty, and all I could do was utter a gentle *ah*.

That sound, let loose, became the most solid, most compact thing in the entire world. My body felt heavy, overwhelmingly so, and I was unable to move. But the rabbits bounded in front of me, racing back and forth, their gracefulness blending into the calmness of the land. Then, another appeared, hopped up on a largish stone and stood motionless, its eyes directed towards me, peering into me. The silence of the scene increased tenfold. One more rabbit jumped into view and the quiet deepened yet again. They came, more and more, and as they did, all sound was evacuated from the world, transforming it into a clear, limpid pool of silence. I turned my head, a movement that now seemed magnified amongst the stillness. My *ah* lingered in the air, not yet absorbed into the sweeping quiet of the landscape. It seemed to persist, perched just above the calm.

I'd been enraptured by nature countless times before, caught in its web, unable to free myself, but I've never been able to put this into words. Nothing but my *ah*... I simply stood there in the midst of all of that confusion and clamour, the chaos swirling about, avid and avaricious. The silence encircled me, stealing the words from my throat. Countless times I'd praised the earth, the wild, but still I could not put into words that there was really no connection between us.

From what I could see, the wild rabbits had mostly blue eyes, except for a reddish trim on the bottom, which I couldn't help but puzzle over. Not long after I learned how the rabbits had come to the area, and, apparently, they weren't indigenous, but rather had been brought by the hydro plant workers earlier in the year, in spring. Unfortunately for them, they cared for the rabbits too well, and their numbers soon exploded. By the time summer rolled around, there were simply too many to keep, so they let them loose to fend for themselves. While some of course died, many proved quite adept at adjusting to life in the wild, so before too much more time had passed, the grasslands around the plant were littered with rabbit holes and a great many more rabbits, each generation more feral than the one before.

Unsurprisingly, Mum was greatly worried about the hordes of rabbits romping across the land, especially since it would soon be harvest season and she wondered how they would protect the yields from such fertile field rodents. As for me, I was more concerned about the approaching winter, which wouldn't be far behind the end of summer. It was still warm enough, of course, and the trees were resplendent with leaves, but once the land and sky froze, what then? Would this world survive? As for the rabbits, well, they weren't truly wild creatures, they'd never experienced a harsh and hostile winter climate, so what difference did it make – most would surely die, wouldn't they?

With these thoughts in mind, I looked once more at the scene in front of me, the rabbits flourishing in the grasses… this might be the final act of their play.

As for Mum's rabbits, after moving up here we kept them in a hutch and wouldn't let them out for any reason. Mum worried they'd run off with the other rabbits; go bad, as it were. Naturally, it was up to me to feed them, so each day I'd sling a basket of alfalfa grass over my shoulder and make sure their stomachs were all full. The rabbits grew way too big, way too fast, however. Before a month had passed, I had to sling two baskets of alfalfa over my shoulder just to make sure they all got their fill.

Although the place where we'd set up the yurt was fairly close to the water, which meant the vegetation was seemingly plentiful and vibrant, it couldn't really stand up to our presence. That is, within a week or so of me feeding our rabbits, there was hardly any alfalfa grass left, at least not nearby. As a result, I had to start walking farther and farther away, sometimes all the way to the northernmost parts of the sunflower fields; on other occasions, I tracked west to the grasslands that stretched to the horizon.

While there were a great number of rabbits, I think there were far more sparrows. In some places, there were thick flocks of what seemed like thousands upon thousands of birds. They'd be perched in a tree, chittering madly before taking to the air in a great swarm to land again in another tree not too far away. Once in a while, you'd see a flock of wild geese fly through the area. They were like a great tide washing onto a beach, powerful and majestic, their enormous wings gracefully keeping them soaring above the ground, a singular flock of birds, bright against the blueness of the sky.

Not even short grasses would grow in the sand dunes of the north; the land would be bright and clean, and devoid of nearly all life. I'd been there, I'd walked over the sand, felt the fine particles work their way into my shoes to travel along with me. Then, standing on top of a dune with the sand spreading out beneath, the vibrant blue sky above, I remember being stunned as before. The ducks near the riverbanks were startled and began to quack, *a! a!*

Amongst the trees, there was a meadow grown thick with dodder. Although it was said the vines were parasitic by nature, there was simply no way I could detest them for they grew so slim and delicate, possessed a pale gold colour and bloomed with small, pure white flowers. Li Bai wrote many poems about dodder, connecting it to love and deep-seated emotions. But the profundity of dodder does not reside only in poetry – it is its fragile, tender form that causes these feelings to well up. I reached down and snipped the alfalfa near the base of the stem, cutting through the dodder that grew upon it. In the corner of my eye, the shadow of a wild rabbit darted by, and I turned my head to get a better look. My body remained where it was. The wind blew forcefully against me, howling past my ears and playing havoc with my hair. The entire world seemed to be submerged in a raging current, tossed about this way and that. I finished picking the alfalfa and stood up. A strange feeling touched my heart. It was as though what I was doing then, so urgently in that singular moment, would resonate millions of years into the future.

32

MOBILE PHONE

My brand-name imitation mobile was cheap, ugly and heavy. I'd also cracked the screen not long after I first got it, if I remember correctly. But whatever I did to it, it kept on ticking, even after I'd dropped it in water I don't know how many times. It's true. I'd fish the damn thing out, and it would still power up. There was even this one time that it sat in water for a couple of hours and I thought for sure it would be dead. But no, after it dried out, it turned on – no problems whatsoever.

It also had a camera that was the envy of anyone who saw it. I mean, there was a slight distortion to the colour of the pics I took, but that only added to the dramatic – I would even say cinematic – quality to the pictures. Its digital amplifier was something to marvel at, too, for the sound it emitted was always crystal clear and perfectly pitched. When I was out in the grasslands gathering alfalfa, I'd always have my phone playing music, and the melodies and tunes would, in turn, carry in the air as though I were at some concert or other.

There were many times I surprised even myself with how much I relied on that cheap imitation phone. Indeed, I never went anywhere without it. And this wasn't because I was afraid of missing some call; I just always had it with me, even in places where

I knew there'd be no mobile signal. I took photos, listened to music, scrolled through previous texts and postings. I was obsessed, too, with our old sunflower fields, obsessed with being alone, as well as with the world that lay just beyond those sunflowers and that loneliness. I suppose in many ways my phone was the... the key... yes, the key to my existence.

But there was one time I lost it.

I discovered it was missing after I'd returned from gathering alfalfa. For a moment, a sense of dread overwhelmed me. I thought I'd lost all connection to my past, that everything had disappeared, and that the path to my future was halted as well. The past and all that was in it, my memories, everything was linked to that phone. And so was what was to come, where my life was headed. My phone *was* everything. I suppose it's no wonder I was as weak as I was...

Finding it wouldn't be easy. The area I'd go to find the wild grasses I needed to feed the rabbits had no mobile service, so I wouldn't be able to phone myself and then narrow in on the ring. I couldn't trace back over the path I'd taken either, since there was no path to follow. Reeds grew everywhere, too, and the wild grasses were just that – wild – and certainly never mowed or trimmed. To make matters worse, the land was terribly uneven, with hills followed by dips followed by more hills. My own habit of keeping my head down didn't help things either as I never really paid much attention to how far I walked – I just went where the alfalfa took me. More than once, I looked up after filling a basket to find out I had no idea where I was.

Uncle and Mum said there was no chance I'd ever find it; the area was simply too vast. It was a case of trying to find the proverbial needle in a haystack. Even a fine-toothed comb would have a hard time locating it amongst the leaves and grasses.

Of course, I knew this already. And it felt as though a part of my heart had been ripped away. I had to look for it... I didn't really have a choice, no matter how futile it seemed.

Three days I scoured the area. As I did, my mind drew me back to the photos I'd taken with the phone, the texts I'd sent and received, the music I'd downloaded. But as I thought about it more and more, my sadness and grief over losing it became increasingly vague and indistinct. My 'loss', however, had only just begun.

My only consolation was that I'd lost it there, in that place, which meant it was unlikely anyone else would ever find it. At least not anytime soon... I mean, except for us and the occasional shepherds who passed through with their cattle, there wasn't another soul around – not even the hydro station workers, who lived relatively nearby, ventured out as far as I'd gone. When harvest time rolled around, we'd pack up our yurt and leave too, let the snow blanket the area and further remove it from the rest of the world. That was what winter meant up here. Years would pass by... who's to say that when someone finally found it, well, they mightn't even know what it was... And besides, it's unlikely that that model of phone would still be in use years from now. Mobile phones might not be around for all we know... it'd be like some ancient artefact...

Who knows how many years might go by... who knows what kind of person might stumble upon it... They wouldn't know any of the songs on my phone, nor would they recognise the importance of the pictures to me, or the telephone numbers, or even the people they might be connected to... I'd lost all connections forever... Whoever that stranger was who found my phone years into the future would just turn it over in his hand a few times and then fling it away... a piece of rubbish... nothing more.

The wind really was quite strong around the river. Especially at night, when we couldn't help but feel that at any moment the yurt would be ripped apart and we'd be left exposed to the wind's ferocity. And if you happened to be out in the wind, you couldn't help but let it drag, push, and pull you along, taking you wherever it wanted to go. It was loud, too, its whistle and whine permeating the sky and the land like some strong current winding its way between heaven and earth. But the yurt was never torn asunder. To our good fortune, the stones we used to anchor it to the ground held firm, so it was unlikely to be cleaved and sent swirling through the air.

That kind of wind never blew for long, either. An hour, maybe two, and then it would die down. But when it did dissipate, the air would be heavy with dust and sand, picked up by the viciousness of the wind to now play havoc with our throats and lungs. Great fits of coughing would be the norm should anyone venture outside, and so usually we didn't, at least not until things settled and we were sure the wind had ceased. The river would then appear to bubble up towards the starry skies, drawn by the dazzling magnificence left in the aftermath of the wind's passage through the area, a great reflection of the Milky Way shimmering in all its glory.

It's true, the stars seemed to shine that much brighter after a fierce wind, and there was a certain crispness to their brilliance, a sharpness not seen before the wind had blown.

Rapt by the scene above, I remember my mind was drawn again to my missing phone. The wind had roared across the land, cleansing it and the sky above of whatever detritus might've lain about, leaving both heaven and earth pristine and beautiful. Perhaps my phone had snapped a picture of it... Perhaps it too longed for such a spectacle? I wondered if it might've taken a picture on its own...

When the wind stopped, my mind fell to worrying about rain. I paid close attention to the changes in the clouds and watched for any signs. And secretly I hoped in my heart of hearts that whatever brush covered my phone would protect it forever, even if it meant I'd never find it.

In the process of searching for my mobile, though it was not successful, I did end up finding quite a few of Chouchou's stolen footwear... and not only shoes but also bits of old, dirty rags and underpants – an assortment of mangled and filthy objects Chouchou had stolen over the course of his time here...

A lot of it was squirrelled away amongst the reeds that grew near the river, as well as amongst the stones and pebbles that lined the riverbank. It was clear he'd gnawed on much of it – the underpants were torn... eh... The only good thing I suppose is that I found them when I did, before he'd destroyed them completely – otherwise, they'd've been fit only for the bin, just as the temperature would start to drop and we'd all be stuck without any extra layers against the cold.

Alongside these finds, I also came across quite a good number of beautiful stones, marked with the most fabulous patterns and interesting shapes. I hadn't expected to find such beautiful objects, and they were all rather heavy, but they were so gorgeous that I couldn't just leave them. In a way it was kind of funny – I'd left the yurt empty-handed in search of my phone, and I'd returned carrying my body weight in stones, my pockets heavy and overflowing. There also remained a pang of regret in my heart over my missing phone.

Still, the stones were beautiful, and as I rolled them over in my hands I grew increasingly surprised at their myriad designs, increasingly enthralled with their beauty. And that's when I found my phone. It had been nestled in amongst these amazing rocks, tightly wedged in between a stunning black and white stone – it was almost as though the rock was what had found my phone; it had protected it for what seemed like forever. It'd been blanched by the sun. I couldn't say how many ants had crawled over it, or how many lizards had puzzled over what it was. In one hand I had my phone, in the other a stone. I was excited beyond compare and incredibly happy.

Finally, I was confused.

33

STONES

I enjoyed collecting stones. Because of this enjoyment, I classified stones into two categories: those that were pretty and those that were not. I suppose it was due to this fondness for collecting stones, too, that my world became a little imbalanced. Luckily, the power of this 'fondness' was relatively weak insofar as it didn't influence my perception of what was real and what wasn't. Most of the influence fell upon what stone I chose, which in turn impacted on the destinies of both types of rock.

I would compare the two types over and over again before finally selecting the one I deemed most beautiful; the other would be discarded. But I always wondered... was the stone that I chose really mine? No, that's not right. I'm not talking about ownership. It was more... more that the stone should be alongside me ever after... I suppose that's what I was getting at... what's the difference between 'avarice' and 'fondness' I wonder?... Each time I found myself outside in the wind, buffeted by the gale, strolling beside the river, I'd direct my eyes to the other side and marvel at the beauty of the rolling, golden sand dunes, at the azure brilliance of the autumn sky. My sight would linger till the sun set, till the fairly translucent moon appeared... and then I would deny those things I once most fervently believed in.

When winter came and I found myself in an even more desolate, more remote place than I had been in before, with nothing but shepherds and their flocks for company, whenever I had a bit of free time, I would immediately take to ambling off into the desert for hours on end, searching for any small stone, rock or pebble that might lie underfoot. When the herdsmen spied me with my multi-coloured stones, saw how fascinated I was with them, they would quickly ask if they were worth any money. I'd answer honestly and say they weren't worth anything, but I would always add that I thought they were beautiful. Usually, this would get me only a suspicious look and then a rueful comment about how it was only us Chinese who knew about such things. In their minds, we were the only ones who bestowed value on rocks. After all, it was us Chinese who drove trucks for hundreds of kilometres to come into the Gobi to collect stones, while they had remained there for generations, content to raise their sheep, to tread over the rocks we Chinese valued, unaware of their worth... There was more regret in his voice when he uttered these last few words, then resignation at the fact that they would probably never understand... the stones they did collect never earned them a cent. In his mind, very few could understand the secret value of rocks. Then he took the stone I was holding and rolled it around in his palm. He regretted his fate more.

"I just like their colours, really. That's it. Look. It's almost a scarlet red!"

My words did nothing to change his mind. He didn't believe me.

When Mum came to visit me in Altay, she'd come with nothing, except two stones carried on her back.

"What the devil do you have there?"

Her look was equal parts mystery and excitement. "Go... bi... jade!"

"And what in hell would I do with it?"

"Nothing... I didn't bring them to give to you... I just wanted you to see them."

It's true. Even my mum started doing it. Everyone in this remote, desolate place began collecting rocks. All across the northern plains, whether there were two hundred and sixteen national highways, or perhaps one more than that, all along them, on either side, quite a few tents cropped up, every hundred kilometres or so, and three out of five were hawking stones. Of course, a great number of the stones were just that – stones, dirty and common in the extreme. That was on the surface, at least. If you were to break them open, however, then the dazzling, dreamlike display of colours would overwhelm you. I often wondered, you know, if their so-called value didn't actually lie in their beauty, but in the contrast between outside and inside? I suppose that's why people started calling them 'Gobi jade'.

There was quite a lot of Gobi jade to be had, too.

Later, when Mum was planning to visit Sichuan, she was stuck thinking about how to make a good impression on her relatives and friends. She had to make it seem as though she was thriving far up here in the north. She had to have something unique to the area, but something that wouldn't put her too much out of pocket. This was all about keeping face and nothing else. I remember watching her as she mulled it over and over. Ultimately, she pried a stone out of the pile that lay at the foot of the wall that surrounded our house, bundled it up and went into the city to find a gemstone workshop. It was a hundred yuan to get the stone cut and made into several bracelets...

She wore one of the Gobi jade bracelets home to Sichuan and awed her family and friends. Once she had handed the others out as gifts, they, too, were all struck by the beauty of the stone then wrapped around their wrists. Most of their expressions were happy and pleased at the gift they'd been given, although there were looks of puzzlement, too.

To be frank, I don't think Gobi jade was all that ideal for jewellery. Its colour was somewhat lacklustre, and it didn't have the same 'pop' as other gems or metals had. I mean, we called it jade but it really wasn't. Actual jade should be that much more refined, exquisite and polished. It had to sparkle, too, in the way that real jade did. I'm not saying that Gobi jade did have a particular beauty, but out here in these wild and desolate plains it was certainly beautiful and it did dazzle. But once you left the wilderness, left the pure blue sky and the rugged earth and stone that stretched beyond the horizon, well, its beauty withered... how could it not?

I once saw Gobi jade in Sanya, on Hainan Island. Nationally speaking, there was no place farther away from Xinjiang than Sanya, so I was surprised to see it. There was a lot of it, too. Two flatbed carts with the stuff piled high. And all of it – pendants and other accessories – was for sale, three pieces for ten yuan. They looked like pieces of plastic, cheap and tacky, mass-produced and worthless.

Was there really a great deal of Gobi jade?

In the beginning... I suppose there was for it seemed as though the numbers of stones far surpassed the great expanse of the wilderness itself – there were rocks everywhere. Even if you were to dig, say, three feet under the ground, you'd find them – and the whole country was like this. Rocks... everywhere... that pile... near our house... I imagine... well... if Mum had pulled them all apart, had taken them all to make bracelets, she'd have enough for tens of thousands. Ha! Three for ten... that's what it meant.

So yeah, there were a lot of rocks, stones wherever you looked... but despite that plenty, despite there being veritable mountains and seas of Gobi jade, there was another side to this story, a story of the problems such plenty brought about. I mean, in the beginning, people would only go out into the countryside on holidays, they'd go for a nature walk, a brisk hike to invigorate the soul, and... well, maybe, while they were out there, they'd collect some rocks... You know, just for fun. They would've parked their vehicles on the side of the highway and wandered off from there, never too far, and never really intent on finding precious stones. No, they would just try their luck and flip over a largish rock to see what was underneath. That was it... there was really nothing to it.

But that's not how things stayed. Soon, more and more people started to come. They brought tools with them, apparatuses to help search for supposedly valuable gems. They'd walk farther and farther, trekking deeper and deeper into the wilderness, scouring the earth for stones they thought could make them some money.

No nook or cranny was left untouched. Then, some began to bring tractors. These were followed by excavators. Things got out of hand... people were just mad about it... that's why they ended up having to sell their Gobi jade three for ten... oversupply killed their market.

Sweethearts out for a leisurely walk, that's who'd buy three. But by the time they got them home, the newness would have worn off and they'd be flung in the corner, soon forgotten. After all, they weren't all that pretty, and they certainly wouldn't appreciate in value. But I knew that these normal stones, these small bits of Gobi jade, had experienced a more rugged, more majestic existence than all the people on this planet. It was as though I'd seen first-hand what they'd been through – the great floods of centuries passed, great droughts, earthquakes. Seawater had attacked them for aeons, had worn them down and then abandoned them to be buried by mud and sand for yet more aeons still. And if that wasn't enough, the wind and the sun would have their turn, too, subjecting them to more torment. And then, finally, they'd been delivered from this oppression, allowed to lie quietly alongside the river, polished and looking fine as though suited up in a seamless dress, embedded in a simple earthen depression, content. Until...

I saw their final act; their last memory. I witnessed how they were violently torn from the earth. The caves that had been their homes exposed. Their insect companions left to scatter at being discovered. The tender roots that had grown about them now subject to the scorching sun. Even more stones were ripped up from the ground by the larger excavators. The ants that had had their nests demolished were at a complete loss, vainly trying to protect the queen and her eggs, their world turned upside down, escape impossible. Isn't the destruction of one ant nest the same as a kingdom being utterly destroyed? The murder of so many insects, the horror of so many tiny lives being snuffed out, their worlds destroyed and nowhere to go, all due to Gobi jade, its colour, its lustre, the tiny cracks across its surface. This is why it was dark. Bloodstained. It was why the jewellery broke, why it would shatter into pieces. But people don't understand this. They don't know why the city streets are so sad and hopeless when the night comes on. The man sifting through the hawker's pieces of Gobi jade does not understand either.

Last year's drought devastated not only the agricultural sector but also the animal husbandry sector. In response to these difficulties, one old shepherd was heard to remark: "Rock collecting! That's what brought this disaster on us... those bastards out collecting stones!"

He was probably right. The explosion of interest in ripping up rocks from the ground had transformed the area, which, when combined with changes in the weather, couldn't help but be connected to the drought that ravaged their livelihoods. It was sort of like fengshui, if we were to think of a Chinese equivalent. I know that's a superstition, but Mum agreed with him, without hesitation. She'd been a victim of the drought, too. She also readily believed any and all explanations as to its cause.

Of course, I should say Mum had also once dreamed of becoming rich by collecting stones. I mean... she lived on the Gobi. She'd seen the trucks come rumbling in, too. These outsiders piercing into the depths of the desert in search of their fortunes. And she'd seen them return heavy with stones, content with what was a productive journey – it was hard for her not to dream of striking it rich in the same way.

But she was too poor. She couldn't risk it on her own. She did try and convince acquaintances to go into business with her. You know, to hire a truck and head-on into the Gobi. But no one ever got back to her, which I think was best. Afterwards, well, the only thing she could do was start farming...

Is there a difference, though, between tearing up the ground to plant sunflowers and tearing up the ground for rocks? Both actions plunder the earth, don't they? One uses machines, and one uses chemicals. They both put a vice-like grip on the land and forcefully extort the last drops of life from it.

I still liked collecting stones. I enjoyed kneeling down on the riverbank, turning whatever stones I had gathered over in my hands. I loved their feel. I was continually amazed, too, over each one's unique beauty. No two were alike. On those occasions, I felt as though I were immersed in Mother Earth, enraptured by the world of these stones. It was like seeing another layer to the planet's existence, like a migratory seabird that tracked ever further ahead, never to lay eyes upon the same reef again. I still do it, you know. I still collect rocks. I see the holes left in the ground after I pick them up. I see the small paths that work their way into the earth. I see the insects scatter as I reveal their underground world to the world above. I know I change their destiny, irrevocably alter what will happen to them. And who's to say I'm not changing more – altering seasons, changing the climate, affecting the amount of snowfall. Maybe I'm even contributing to the melting of the glaciers, or the retreat of colder weather. Maybe I'm even playing a role in global warming. I don't know.

But the planet is getting hotter. Water levels are rising. I'm witnessing that seabird search in vain for new land. I see it consume all of its energy. I see its hopelessness. I see it disappear into the ocean. But in this place where my feet are, so far removed from the seas and oceans, the remotest of locations deep in the land, I still saw another beautiful stone. This time I didn't dare touch it.

34

THINKING OF THE ULUNGUR

The Ulungur runs in a northerly direction through land that oh so desperately needs it. There are, actually, a great number of rivers in the north, but there are none in the south. It is the final boundary marker, the last shielded area before the land opens up to the southern expanse of wilderness, the last place to find shelter. The gazelles that tromp far and wide know the river. They know its path and its importance; they congregate in herds upon its banks to drink its life. The crows and ravens know of the river, too. They perch contentedly in the short trees that reach up from the middle of it. There are river otters as well, playful creatures that enjoy the shallows, their heads just above the water, their eyes attentive of everything.

The river starts in the east, with the glaciers that cap the mountains there; it ends in the west, emptying into the great lake that bears the same name. Ulungur Lake is the last vestige of the ancient sea that once covered the area. Its vast calmness echoes that of millions of years ago. Its azure water is clear and lucid. There is an almost unearthly quality about the lake, perhaps something from long ago that's been forgotten. Small islands dot the surface of the water. They provide sanctuary to migratory swans and sea mews, and places to breed. Their eggs, delicate and precious, are hidden under the thick brush that covers the islands like warm blankets. Life beneath the waters is forever quiet and still, separate from the world above. Reeds grow along the banks, strong, powerful and imposing. The desert beyond them is pure white. Grey fossils of ancient organisms populate the great expanse that rolls out beyond the lake. Further still, mountains rise up in great ranges that run beyond the horizon. They're young mountains, the youngest on the planet. I suppose that was... something, the oldest waterway in the world lying next to the youngest mountain range.

I was on the bus when I passed the large body of water, and in many ways it felt like those thousands of years ago when men passed by the same spot on camelback. The closer I drew to the lake, the more memories flooded back. It was as though everything that had happened for the last thousand years came rushing to the fore. But the bus never stopped, and soon the water receded behind me, taking its memories with it, one after the other. The four wheels rolled on, its speed increased, and I was carried helplessly along with it.

The feeling of awe I felt when seeing the Ulungur stayed with me. I marvelled at how the river flowed determinedly, obstinately over the parched, desolate landscape, how it worked its way over the earth and how life clung to it desperately, how villages of people did the same. I was awed by their courage; the romance of it all.

I walked on this good earth and felt nothing else but awe. It suffused my body, filled every nook and cranny of my clothes, my being. If I were to be suddenly shorn of this feeling, I'd have nothing. Life would become as light as a feather. It'd twist and turn in the wind, and then be gone. There are millions upon millions of me, all feeling the same way, all carried off by four-wheeled machines into...

I did once more draw close to the water out here in the wilderness, and it did again play havoc in my heart of hearts, thrashing me about most violently. I remember a great wind blew, whipping up the lake and its river. I felt as though I were being whipped and tossed about by the wind, too. Once more as light as a feather, my soul caught in the whirlwind and rocked about. I stood as best I could on the highest bank, swaying in the wind, mesmerised by this moment in time, enraptured but yet somehow not satisfied. High up, I could see both sides of the river as they opened wide to the expansive desolation beyond. I could see in every which direction how its tributaries had died in the arid wilderness – the paths they took covered with long-dead traces of water. There had been so many riverbeds, so much water... once, long ago... but now only one remained. I looked over the barren, crisscrossed riverbanks and imagined the return of life, a great rushing flood that would transform the landscape. I fantasised, too, about a charging army of a thousand horses following ancient roads... I stared into the west... Ulungur Lake was calm and quiet, stretching farther than my eyes could see.

A married woman bedecked in red, pulling a cow along with her, passed the area, singing as she walked. When she came closer to me, she smiled shyly, bearing but a sliver of her white teeth. Gradually, she disappeared into the distance, and all I could think was that I had so much to tell her... but I'd been too shy myself to say anything.

35

HONEYBEES

Mum was always so genuine and honest. She would wave sweetly to all visitors whether she knew them or not, and treat them as though they were close friends – family even. She had a unique skill, you could say, in ascertaining one's profession and how best to call them. As a result, she never once struggled with trying to remember names, never once feared making a mistake. If they worked in the mines extracting coal, she'd refer to them as a coal boss; if they worked with bricks, she'd call them a bricklayer; if they raised rabbits then they were a boss of that... Of course, if the latter didn't fancy the name, they'd just pretend they didn't hear her. Our nearest neighbours – those who tilled the land like Mum –were all referred to as 'land bosses'. As for those taking care of bees, well, they were naturally called beekeepers.

The beekeeper that'd come this year was from the south. He'd travelled so far to such a remote place, carrying his bees with him. How did he know there were great fields of sunflowers planted near the Ulungur River? How did he know, too, that there were no bees, nor any beekeepers, in the area? Okay... I guess there wasn't really any point in me being worried about him. But I couldn't help but think that what he was doing was 'heroic'. He and his thousands of bees were nomads, wanderers... there was an affinity there...

Once the sunflowers blossomed, the job of pollinating them was of the greatest importance. Each year when that season rolled around, everyone would participate in the work, whether they were beekeepers or not. Now, if all you had was a few mu of sunflowers, the work would be quite easy – all you would need to do was line the flowers up face-to-face and that would be it. If you had a whole field of sunflowers, that was a different matter altogether, and the work would be correspondingly that much more intense. Of course, this would also mean the monies paid out to hired hands would increase, too. In such situations, everyone ended up relying on the bees, these rather tiny creatures.

"Have you ever seen large-scale bee farms?" Mum asked. "The flowers would have to become a bright golden yellow before the beekeeper would come. He'd bring his beehives and first survey the area to find a suitable place to lay them down. Once satisfied, he'd position the boxes on the ground and then open them. The bees would emerge from inside... Oh my... they would be a great swarming horde, the drone of their wings drowning out every other sound... It was soooo beautiful! The whole sky was!"

But the challenges of this year were a foregone conclusion. And we were right in the middle of it, if for no other reason than that much of the land to the south had already been abandoned. The losses the farmers had endured had been disastrous. Complicating matters was the increase in price for fertiliser, as well as the hired-worker fees. The plague of destructive insects was also serious. Most families had already spent far more than usual on pesticides, which meant there was very little by way of disposable income amongst the so-called 'land bosses'.

Although hiring itinerant workers to tend to the pollination of the fields was cheaper than having permanent employees, one mu did cost twenty yuan, and so several hundred wasn't exactly inexpensive. We only had our small field, unlike many of our neighbours, but still we had to spend a few thousand.

I don't know where the rule came from, or what regulation it was, but purchasing fertiliser and pesticides could be done on credit. That wasn't the case for hired hands overlooking bees; they had to be paid, in cash, when the work was complete; no exceptions. Unsurprisingly, when that day came, those responsible for handing out the cash couldn't help but be incredibly anxious. Mum's heart would skip a beat when she saw the beekeeper show up at her door looking for payment. She would on some occasions fantasise about trying to, quietly, rat on her debt...

"I've only this small bit of land, and look at how the flowers have grown. What nerve he's got to come here looking for money? Ha... it doesn't matter anyway... I've no money to give him. I suppose he could tie up their wings and keep the bees away from my field, couldn't he?" Even if what she thought was rather... dishonest... rascally even, there was some meaning behind it; it did make some sense. I learned later on, however, that the beekeeper wasn't that dumb! Before he released any of his bees, he'd require payment up front. If even one family didn't have cash to pay, he'd refuse to release even a single bee. There wasn't really any need for him to pressure someone into paying since the other farmers would take on that... responsibility... come hell or high water. Time, too, was of the essence. If money wasn't turned over, if the sunflowers weren't pollinated in swift fashion, then the opportunity would quickly be lost, the seeds would fall fallow, and the fields would ultimately die. Of course, the sense of urgency didn't belong solely to the farmers. It was an anxious time for the beekeeper, too. He had to collect payment from everyone, which meant he had to walk the length and breadth of the ten thousand mu. He had to knock on all the doors, drink the tea offered him, chat and listen to them grumble and complain. That's when he learned whether or not the families he spoke to had the money to cover his expenses, whether they were really poor or not, and the gamble involved in taking them on as customers.

His bet was on the flowers, on the harvest, while the farmers bet on the bees. Putting it in these words, I suppose they shared the same anxieties. The beehives were there. But they remained shut. The lives of the bees inside rested on the small bit of white sugar the beekeeper had put in with them. The only problem was the sugar wouldn't last, nor could the bees eat too much of it for ultimately it would poison them.

I don't know who first compromised. But the bees were finally released. When I saw them take to the sky in a great droning swarm, I couldn't help but remark that Mum was right – it was a beautiful sight! Not long after, the fields, all ten thousand mu, were aglow with millions of gold and black bees dancing to and fro. Even the sound of their continuous buzz added to the brilliance. The buzz was unrelenting and soon drowned out all other sounds. If you listened to it carefully, it seemed like a great net extending out in all directions, enveloping the sky and blanketing the land. Besides the sun, the air, and the incessant buzz, everything else was swallowed up by this great pristine net.

The sky was the heaviest lid. The buzz was the second. Both weighed upon our heads. The atmospheric pressure changed, and we felt as though we were quickly burning up. First, our ears felt the heat, then our moods. This continued into the night so that our sleep was similarly tortured...

All Mum could say was how beautiful it was. But this was perhaps all anyone could say; it was so beautiful!

Beautiful...

Mum was unmistakably pleased. "Once the flowers are pollinated, we can buy our own honeybees! We must purchase local bees. That's how we'll get the purest of honey... one kilo sells for twenty yuan!"

I rolled this over in my mind, but something didn't seem right. There was a note of indignation in my voice as I challenged her. "Then why the hell did we work so hard on that land... waiting for the flowers to blossom, wasting all that money on hiring bees... and then wasting more on buying the honey they made as a result of pollinating our sunflowers?" I paused, and my mind returned suddenly to the land we'd abandoned in the south. Not only had the water been stopped, but by this time there were certainly no bees in the area... it was thoroughly lost.

"Ah... don't worry about it..." There was a particular resignation in Mum's voice. "There's nothing to be done anyway." Then her voice changed and took on a slightly mysterious tone. "Relax... wherever there're flowers, there're certain to be bees. That's just the way it goes. Besides, we grew sunflowers – proper big ones – and their scent travels far and wide, making them easy for the bees to find." That's when she told me about what happened the year before.

It was, in short, a catastrophic year. She tilled the land, repeatedly, but there had never been enough water... and then there'd been that... that 'spot' – every farmer who'd seen the same thing before said it bode misfortune, the sign of a sickness that could not be treated, at least not easily...

Why be worried! Mum couldn't help but shoot from the hip. Practically every farmer had lost substantial sums last year. At first, Mum thought she was in the same boat as the rest of them. It was fortunate we only had the two hundred mu. Yes, she lost out, but not by as much as others with far more land did. It was that good fortune that allowed us to survive. Our sunflowers produced enough – maybe not as much as before, but enough to leave us with seeds for the future. That's how Mum was able to sow the fields the following year and save a little money by not having to buy new seeds. A short time after, Mum discovered that she was not in the red – she'd actually broken even!

Because of the weak and wanting harvest, the supply of seeds that year did not meet demand. As a result, those in possession of seeds from before now increased their prices – at first marginally, but finally doubling them...

With the price of sunflowers increasing over the past couple of years, Mum was predictably pleased. Each time she sat down to eat, she'd have not only her bowl but also a slate of wood so that she could do calculations while she ate. The more she ran the numbers, the more things looked better and better. She'd estimate the yield per each mu of land, then value the yield and figure out how much of it could be sold. Next, she factored her costs, how much to invest... Finally, she compared the numbers with what she had in the beginning, and it seemed as though she had quite a significant amount in reserve. This reserve would be her profit... but then, what was the missing cost she'd not factored in?

She mulled this over and over for a while... and then suddenly realised what it was, the only thing that made sense... the bees! And the beekeeper!

Traditionally, one of the more prominent farmers in the region took charge of organising this vital service, and they would, in turn, accompany the beekeeper when he made his rounds, informing the other farmers of what had been arranged and how much each had to pay. But this year, every farmer in the area was feeling the pinch – they had exhausted whatever monies they'd had, and thus no one had thought of sorting out the bees.

This state of affairs caused no small amount of grief for Mum! She'd worked her arse off to get through the year, and now the little bit of money she had left was owed to the beekeeper! Finished! That's what she felt. She threw the bowl to the ground, smashing it to pieces... then howled out loud. "I've seen the bloody bees!" But that was it... the sky really wasn't all that beautiful anymore. She'd seen enough.

The faint golden hue of the sunflower seeds bounded this way and that in the fields as though trying to pick and choose where to go. The buzz of the bees that had enveloped the area could not last. Things started to go quiet, and then virtually nothing could be heard. The heat had dissipated. So too had the excitement. The swarm of bees grew faint, barely discernible in the sky. It'd been enough. For these bees, these golden coloured imps, it was enough. The farmers had abandoned the land, even if they had not forgotten about the harvest. Mum stared out at the horizon, at the unending landscape that seemed to stretch on forever.

Whose bees were they? How had they known about the flowers? How had they found this place? How had they travelled thousands of kilometres across barren wilderness... It's remained a riddle to this day.

And last year... Mum had been focused on twenty yuan a kilo for good honey... but she'd never bought any.

36

THE COLOUR OF GOLD

The bees came, and the fields bloomed a brilliant, golden yellow. It was as though we were transported back to ancient times, the golden gates of the kingdom opening wide, the drums echoing a joyous memorial to the emperor, the pitch of their voices growing louder and resonating through the air, the majesty of the spectacle reaching its apex... In the great illumination of the ten thousand mu of sunflower fields, summertime was declared to be at its end. The grand splendour of autumn was to begin.

I was reminded of Granny's lonely appraisal of the sunflowers in bloom – how beautiful they were, how dazzling. Thinking of her again brought me back to other thoughts... Why had she just died? Why did she feel the need to leave? Granny... just look... the world you left hasn't changed at all... The sunflowers you were so infatuated with still bloom the way they had when you were alive. Their brilliance could still be seen at the same time as always... Can you still see their golden petals in death?

On these great northern plains, the end of summer and the beginning of autumn signalled the time of plenty when each and every small town and village basked in enormous wealth. Each tree in the area was akin to the proverbial money tree, all the colour of gold – most especially the white birch for it possessed not only golden leaves but also white silver ones. And not just its foliage, but its trunk, too – in fact, the whole tree dazzled, and when it swayed in the wind it radiated this brilliance in all directions. It's true there was a scarlet tinge to its magnificent gold, and an azure hue to its silver, but this detracted little from its magnificence. It stood, tall and imposing, like some great desire not easily sated. A tree half-swallowed by the autumn, then transformed into something else towards autumn's close. But that didn't matter either, for in amongst these two halves of the same tree, there was the eternal white birch that no autumn could fully squander. For countless years, since time immemorial, the white birch of the northern plains was what men hungered for; it's what drew them into the great expanse, into the abyss.

If the golden hue of these trees symbolised being thrust into some abyss, the colour of wheat fields near harvest time was of a deeper, more comforting shade. That was the power of something that could provide sustenance. Man's fate, his will, his courage and passion were tied up with this. The rolling waves of wheat in the wind, the meandering spread of their fields – on this great land, only the light of day could rival their splendour.

The yellowish tint to pasturing lands can be seen at higher elevations. The men who make use of it are the shepherds who pull their carts back and forth between the wilderness and the small villages they reside in. They harvest the grass, and before long their heads are all adorned with a greenish conical hat that soon turns a pale yellow colour as the grasses dry and harden. The path from green to yellow is one marched many times before by all manner of leaves and grasses; it is as natural as nature can be. But for a village and its inhabitants, it is more than the passage of night through a dreamland of fantastic transformations. After a hard day's work, the men are exhausted and readily welcome sleep. When they awake, they discover their town stands at the precipice of autumn; one step outside their front door is one step into the abyss. The grasses remain high and somehow separate from reality, alight for all eternity.

But the gold colour of reeds is entirely bound up with the

watery banks on which they grow. Reeds are always the companions to rivers, their colours intimately connected with the ebb and flow of the water that gives them life. Their colour is thus weak and fragile, tender and helpless. But hidden in this tenderness is a great secret, a beauty that forces men into halting their steps forward. They crane their heads to stare off into the distance, and the waterfowl cry out in long and short bursts.

The gold of the moon has a darkish hue. Most people believe there's a connection between the moon and their hometown, a link to years past, to their youth. But the truth is, the only connection is between the moon and the night. Man's fondness for the moon and the cultural meanings he gives to it are refused at the door – left outside – for the moon is uninterested in them. It loves its loneliness, its freedom.

The most infinitesimal gold is the colour of honeybees. Their gold is but fragmentary, drawn along by the blond magnetism. They're the golden key that opens the golden lock. Their resplendence has much to do with the sweetness they hold in their mouths. Honey also possesses a golden hue. Each mouthful contains the millions upon millions of kilometres of gold that swirls in the world around us.

And in amongst this golden splendour, the sunflower slowly ascends to the throne, master of all. The beginning of autumn signals this majesty. Heaven and earth become unbalanced, what was up becomes down, what was down becomes up. The sky grows bluer and bluer. There is nothing in nature left to describe it. Only in the man-made world can we find a suitable descriptor – the blue is that of so many car registration plates across China... That distinct blue contrasted with the white numbers...

Gold and blue like this ancient watery planet alone in the cosmos. And in between steps forth man, suddenly aware of his unblemished visage...

37

SAND DATES

In advance of the rush that preceded the sunflowers maturing, there was a rush instead for sand dates, which promised to be a bumper crop. When Mum finished her work in the fields, she'd pass by a forest of wild-growing trees heavy with dates, often stopping for a spell to pick some of the fruit. The dates weren't for us to eat, however, as Mum would bring them home and then summarily crush them in front of the door. A second after doing this, the chickens would all come racing forward and plunge their sharp beaks into the pulpy mess, making such a noise that one couldn't help but wonder if the sky were truly falling or if some other calamity was about to transpire. Mum would stand and watch, wholly gratified by the scene like a young Lei Feng watching an operatic piece.

Gosh, how were there so many sparrows in this region! Every wintry morning after they arose from their slumber, they'd shake off the snow upon their wings as though it were a quilt and then immediately hop towards the nearest wild date tree to enjoy their breakfast. Their little heads would twist and twirl, first to the left to peck at the dates that were there, then to the right to do the same thing. Once they cleared the area closest to their mouths, they would use their little claws to rake in the next closest dates and continue to gorge themselves. They'd eat for about half a day, and during all of that time they'd not see a single other sparrow. That's not because there were none around, but rather that none would raise their heads while they ate.

Once finished, it was only natural that they should require a digestive aid, which meant the wintry forest whence they awoke grew rather loud and raucous. Some would drop in on others; some would simply wave; while still others would fall into arguing. Afterwards, they'd all break out into song – a chaotic, disorganised cacophony moving from tree to tree in flurried haste. When I found myself walking underneath those date trees, I could imagine the sheer joy and delight the sparrows partook in. I could see their small, dark eyes, their plump little bodies and their oh-so-common feathers that had the look of a well-worn overcoat. I pitied their short lifespan, almost forgetting that mine wasn't all that much longer.

Walking through the date tree forest, I could see the fruit, heavy and ripe, above me, very similar in shape to large grapes. They were so heavy, in fact, that they caused whole branches to noticeably droop. It was like the trees were being pulled continuously towards the ground.

I suppose this plenty wasn't solely for the sparrows but could be for me as well. At least, that was how it looked from my point of view, that's how it filled my memory. I walked amongst the trees. I picked the dates and ate them, too. I wasn't the only one, either. Saihu and Chouchou enjoyed the dates as well, although I don't know how they learned the small fruit was safe to eat. I imagine they must've stumbled across some of the heavier dates that had already fallen to the ground; they would've smelled them, sampled them on their tongues and ultimately discovered they were good to eat. After that, well, there were more than enough of the dates lying about to fill their bellies if they so chose. One, bite, two, gulp and they would be gone, pit and all.

I learned some time before that there were two types of dates.

One type was a greyish, white colour, about the size of a soybean. Unlike the soybean, however, these were sweet and juicy, especially the small bit at the top that was almost translucent – that was the sweetest part. All you had to do was carefully open them up, and the sweet, juice-like honey would seep out like tears. These were the dates people found the most delicious, the most fragrant. The only regrettable thing about them was that they were rather small. In fact, if one removed the pit, there wasn't really that much flesh to eat. One bite... you'd taste that sugary nectar, and then by the second bite your teeth would land on that bare rock-like seed at the centre.

The second type was much more common. Their colour was somewhat reddish; they were also plumper and very pretty. Because of their larger size, they sated one's appetite that little bit more than their greyish cousins. Their texture, however, wasn't nearly as pleasing. By any measure, they were nowhere near as sweet. In truth, they were somewhat bland, akin to eating dry flour... probably mixed with sand... I guess that wasn't altogether surprising considering where we were.

From this, I suppose you could see the fairness of creation. It was something I had first learned when I was a child. But, in this place, near this large reservoir, I'd been forced into rethinking things. The dates here in this remote location were not observing the balance and fairness of heaven and earth – they were both large and sweet! They really were! Now... if I'd not eaten them, if I'd let them be... it'd be a different story, and I would never have known. But I did try them... I tasted them, and I couldn't help but wonder if they weren't some crossbreed between a date and a jujube... how else could their size be explained? How else could they've tasted so delicious?

In the northern heart of the continent, I fully believe that these date trees featured prominently in childhood memories. They were perhaps the most important memory. I can't imagine a single student failed to mention the trees at least once in their primary school homework. That includes me... and my mum. The only piece of work Mum had received praise for was a prose essay on the flowering of the date trees. There was one sentence in particular that still resonated with her: "The date trees have bloomed, and their fragrance permeates the air about the school." Half a century later she could still recall it, word for word. I don't know, I suppose this was the most romantic period in her life, the time in which she felt most passionate.

I also sang the praises of the dates, how they grew out of nowhere and flourished only by means of their own enthusiasm. But today, that fervour of youth had waned, although I was still willing to extol them – unconditionally, unendingly.

That time I strolled through the date trees by myself, I could see the fruit hanging everywhere, heavy and ripe, branches almost overburdened with plenty. They were like a jubilant crowd pushing to the front of the line, cheering loudly at the head of state who'd deigned to visit their corner of the world. I, in turn, sought to placate the jubilation of the masses. "Comrades," I spoke out loud to the trees, "I know you've worked tirelessly. I recognise your sacrifices." I stuffed another date into my mouth and another after that. I knew I should stop, but I couldn't. I knew the back of my throat would be scoured raw by the tartness of the dates… but that never happened, and nor did I reciprocate the great kindness shown to me by the date trees.

I continued to eat, more and more, but a creeping sense of shame welled up inside me. The dates I had been gorging on might very well be the whole of what the sparrows could eat this winter! But then I spun my head around, scanning every which direction… What a spectacular feast they would have! There was absolutely no way they could eat all of the fruit. I reckoned they could even invite the crows to dine with them and still be unable to finish the entire spread. I made a point of remembering this place. I imagined I could one day return, bring my closest friends with me, permit them to see, first-hand, the miracles this vast wilderness contained, and encourage them to draw close to their own deep loneliness that they had tried in vain to escape from…

That's right – there were still dates. They were the other miraculous feat you could find up here in the middle of nowhere. I longed for them, I'll admit it. And it was a terrible longing, deep and suffocating. Only someone who's caught the whiff of their spring fragrance can describe what they're really like, and only those who have tasted them in the autumn can truly put into words what they smell like in spring – these are the only people who know what I mean, the only ones who really understand what a date is. To grasp what this legendary tale says about this barren, inhospitable land out here in the heart of central Asia, in this land that stretches unparalleled in all directions, these hormonally fantastic trees stand obstinate against nature, urging this dry land into new life. Each time a tree flowers, each time the fruit ripens is the advancement of all life, but only the date is born from the many tales in *The Arabian Nights*. Only that has emerged from between gold and silver coins; only that has found the ancient paths along the Mediterranean, in the passionate love between man and woman that so graces *One Thousand and One Nights*.

The dates were used to protecting themselves and grew spikes over their outer skin. It was as though they were always prepared to welcome harm. But on this good earth, the feelings of loyalty and friendship were formed through conflict and strife – in battle is where relationships matured. After all, think of the rose, think of the sand date. Their thorns prick, and yet we love them so.

The tree's roots went deep into the driest of dry earth, They're defined by their struggle to leech water from the land, so their pace of growth is exceptionally slow and languid. Yet even if they exhaust nearly all of the energy searching for moisture, their leaves still retain touches of green; they hang on to life, no matter how hard it may be. Small, small leaves, oh so fragile and small. Tiny, tiny yellow flowers accompanied by even tinier fruit. The sand date tree uses the smallest of fingers to pry open the most majestic of energies. The trees have blossomed!

I have come to know many strong fragrances – French perfume, blossoming sand date trees. But it is the latter, out here in this wilderness, that allows for young orphaned love to finally find its resting place, to finally stop wandering. And when those flowers ripen, the sand date perfume is only too willing and happy to retreat into the deepest of recesses, into the pit, for it knows all problems lessen with the passage of time.

I continued to eat the dates and wondered if the sparrows knew what love was, if they'd ever experienced it. The common sparrow is but a lowly bird. It tweets and squeaks, for a time, and then its life comes to its end. As for the other bird raised amongst the sand date trees – the crow – its stature is larger than that of the sparrow, so presumably it has a more voracious appetite. Crows are bedecked in black and give off a vibe of strength and formidableness. It's somewhat odd, I suppose, that we consider its caw nothing but clamorous noise; that its very appearance bodes ill. But when it takes to the air, it does so as every other bird; its gracefulness in the air is as resplendent as any other fowl.

What of its love?

A murder of crows circle in the air. In the distance, wild geese embark on a journey. The arrival of autumn is akin to the grandness of the king ascending his throne. And in that splendiferousness I continued to devour date after date, all the while turning things over in my mind... Were there enough dates for everyone till the end of winter?

BATHING

Saihu was terrified of being given a bath. But she'd lived out in the wilderness for so long now... and her fur was white... the longer she went without a bath, the more serious things would become. Luckily her... clothing... was what we could call a... a renewable resource in that it continued to grow, which meant Mum was forever getting her shears out to cut off the dirty spots. I suppose it was more convenient than bathing her. By the middle of summer, however, Saihu was suffering greatly from mange, and red sores mottled her skin. The only treatment was to rub cocklebur over her flesh in the hope it would neutralise the scabies parasite. Poor Saihu... she'd reached middle age and was now facing the most difficult, most dire predicament she could. To complicate things even more, the fur on her underbelly had become so filthy that new follicles ceased to grow and her nipples grew black and hard...

Saihu would often squat outside the front door and angle her head up towards the sky to bask in the sun. When she did so, her crusted, blackened nipples drew the attention of some of the old chickens that scurried this way and that. The inquisitive chicken couldn't help but shift closer to Saihu as she continued to sunbathe, drawn by the curious black-bean-like growths on her belly. The fowl stared for what seemed like half a day, then, once satisfied with its judgement concerning the small, blackish growths, it moved with surprising speed, a lightning strike... with incredible accuracy... and clamped its beak over poor Saihu's nipples...

The way she yelped and howled will stay with me forever.

Chouchou was precisely the opposite. He enjoyed a bath two or three times a day... a real clean freak. Mum cursed the animal daily – she'd never seen such a stupid dog before. The weather was growing increasingly cold – there were even night frosts – and still Chouchou, the moron, according to her, would wake every morning and plunge himself into the river, frolicking about like a child in the bath. He'd swim back and forth, enjoying the water to no end, only his great head visible in the rushing current.

"Not afraid of the cold weather... hmm? You crazy, bloody beast... What kinda animal doesn't know the difference between hot and cold?" Mum clutched her padded winter clothes tightly around her body and continued to berate poor, stupid Chouchou.

I didn't really understand why she was behaving the way she was. Compared to that business with the shoes... well, why get angry over his penchant for bathing? I suppose it was more that she feared the cold... and figured that everyone else, people and dogs, ought to be the same.

To be honest... well... I'd never seen another dog that enjoyed water like Chouchou. It didn't matter what kind of body of water it was, either – a small stream, a larger river, a puddle on the side of the road – all it took was for Chouchou to see it and then he bounded excitedly into it, regardless of its depth, or its shallowness. Afterwards, once he'd had his fun, he'd climb out of whatever body of water he'd jumped into and shake himself dry with the same sort of vigour and enjoyment. He'd saunter back over towards us then, absolutely guilt-free, as though what he'd done was completely okay.

Chouchou had a large frame, fierce and ferocious looking. As he tromped along the road, he looked more like an awe-inspiring wolf of the plains than a mere canine. Needless to say, he struck fear into most people who saw him. That was until he acted the fool, and then his wolf-like appearance was soon forgotten.

Chouchou also greatly enjoyed acting the spoilt child, but considering his impressive frame and the danger he could cause, this wasn't as cute as it could have been – first he charged about, then he slammed his head into whatever was closest, and then he reached up on his hind legs and planted his front paws on one of us, causing us to buckle under his weight. At the same time, his tail would be sticking straight out into the air, wagging vociferously. On these occasions, Chouchou lost any sense of pity people might've had for him. All they would feel was the greatest of desires to pull themselves away from his cumbersome embrace and spin 360 degrees away from him. Of course, the problem was who had the strength to do it! Chouchou was just so massive, so powerful. All I could do whenever Chouchou decided to play the part, whenever he became the monster instead of the great, beautiful tobet he could be, was to howl as loud as I could so that the nearby hydro plant workers couldn't help but hear my distress (and hopefully come to my aid).

In all likelihood, you couldn't've got much more remote and lonely than the hydro plant. It wasn't the most difficult place to work, either, which meant from time to time the workers would drop by and pay us a visit. There was one young woman who was especially warm and welcoming. She'd come every couple of days to see me. I don't know why she enjoyed my company, nor did I understand why I liked hers, but I imagine it had something to do with the fact that we were both quite lonely.

It's possible, too, that she thought we weren't that well off, that we didn't really have much to eat. I don't really know, but on those days she did come to see me she would only ever see a few vegetables on the table, some cabbage maybe, and not much else. That would explain why she started to bring leftovers from the workers' canteen – some fried pancakes, dumplings, stuff like that. If she'd been to the city, there were even times when she brought fruit and other types of street food like pork sausages and anything else deep-fried.

She'd ask for some flowers in return. On one of her more recent visits, I remember, the flowers had just begun to blossom and mature. I escorted her deep into the sunflower fields so she could choose her own. When we were finished, she had a great dish of flowers, filled nearly to overflowing.

Seeds from fresh sunflowers taste a lot like young walnuts. Their skins are equally soft and tender; they're not terribly greasy either, but instead sweet and moist.

We held the dish of flowers with both hands and picked out the seeds as we walked. We were quite dextrous, I believe, for we peeled the seeds and ate them as we strolled through the fields... and talked... and talked... teasing out minute details from each other's lives, until we got to how much she made and then we stopped. Still, a great deal was revealed, which brought us closer together.

Each time she departed, she would warmly invite me over to her dormitory. Each invitation came with the info that her dorm was equipped with showering facilities that I could use if I so wished. I can't really explain why she was so kind to me. Nor did I understand why she kept mentioning the shower. Then, some days later, I happened to see my reflection... I understood things after that...

It'd been... I'd say a month or more since my last shower. When the weather was hot outside, I'd just close the door to our yurt, soak a face towel in water and wash my face that way. Sometimes I'd boil some water and wash my hair, too. But working out in the fields, well, most farmers didn't pay their appearance much attention. After all, it's not like you'd bump into people when tilling the land... My train of thought took me to my mum, then. I don't know why, but I couldn't help but feel on guard about something.

But moving here... near to this reservoir... it made accessing water that much easier. A helluva lot more convenient, too. I mean, I went to fetch water daily. The small tributary wasn't far from where we set up the yurt. It was just a little to the south, past a copse of reeds. The only issue, however, was that the water was rather muddy. We had to let it sit for more than a day before it was clean enough to use.

Also, there was this one time... when I went out into the fields to look for Mum. I just started walking along the stream, heading in the direction of its lower reaches, following it west for about a kilometre or so. That's when I discovered an even smaller tributary branching off from the stream. It wasn't all that big – much narrower and shallower than the main stream – but it was far cleaner, and it had a much slower current. Its riverbed was filled with clear white stones, which helped to explain the nature of the water. There were reeds lining the riverbanks, as well as some small shrubs.

It was a much nicer spot for our yurt... that was certain.

After the Mid-Autumn Festival, the temperature suddenly rose. Although it was still cold early in the morning and late in the day, the middle of the day was incredibly hot. It was like that for two days, and with the mercury going so high, my mind was drawn to that small tributary and whether or not I should steal away to bathe in it. The reeds were thick enough, and the only other living creatures nearby were the cattle and sheep. It was far enough away, too, from any town or village, as well as the farming fields. I figured there was no way anyone would stumble upon me so exposed. So when the sun was highest in the sky, when the temperature was as warm as it was going to be, I took a clean change of clothes and some soap and headed off to the small stream nestled amongst the reeds.

No one else knew where I'd gone. It couldn't have been more secluded. But when I tested the water as it ran there under the blazing sun, who could've known it would be cold enough to freeze a person solid? Well, I suppose that's not entirely true. I should've known – it was September after all, and the mornings and nights were terribly cold. Ice had been seen in the water closer to home, and it did run down hundreds of kilometres from the glaciers higher up.

I hadn't even finished washing my feet before I had to give up... I was just too bloody cold... There was nothing left to do but pack up my clothes and head back to the yurt.

My disappointment with the stream meant that the next time the young hydro plant worker invited me over to her dorm to shower, I immediately agreed and thanked her accordingly. I grabbed my clothes and sandals just as quickly, and together we walked off towards the bathroom. It wasn't long before I noticed that we weren't, in fact, going to her dormitory but rather the on-duty machine room. Apparently, it had been the communal shower in the past.

In the beginning, there weren't many people working at the hydro plant, and most of them would wait until their shift rotation to shower back at home in the city. Of course, this meant the shower facilities had been left unused. Inside the machine room, there were great, monstrous pieces of equipment, numerous rotating wheels, as well as all manner of pipes and tubes. Off in the corner was the entrance to an adjoining tunnel. We walked over to it, and she lifted the iron bar that spanned across the door. Then she gestured for me to follow her into the dark passageway. The steps were narrow and long, and I couldn't see a thing. At the bottom, another security door awaited us. As we drew close to it, I could hear the metallic clang of the machines inside. Once she opened the door, the sound grew louder, echoing off the walls, drowning out all other sounds. I felt as though I'd been spirited away into some large machine-based world.

The room felt large, but it was too dark to really tell. Even when she turned on the lights that hung precariously from the tiled roof, the darkness didn't abate – it only seemed to absorb the light and keep us surrounded in shadow. I could see everything, but I couldn't make out what anything was. The machines clanged and clanged; a deafening dissonance of metallic clamour that ingested every other sound. I held back, not daring to step any further into the room. The din was emanating mostly to the right of me. In the same direction were the valves for the dam. I knew that over there in the dark there was water gushing violently over huge mecha-nised wheels. I knew that the speed at which the wheels churned was vital to the generation of power, and that the electricity created was violent, frenetic and not generally easy to control... And yet, the machines over there in the dark were doing specifically that, controlling and binding the electricity for human use. The power would be shunted into receptacles and along densely packed wired piping. It was all around us. The air was practically alive with electricity; there... in the dark... I could feel it. Even more was confined in the large instruments overhead, where it was processed and then manoeuvred into the lines that wound their way out of the dam and off into the broad, wide expanse, finally lighting the rooms and powering the electrical devices in thousands and tens of thousands of homes.

I felt terrified at man's power. I could also feel, however faintly, the touch of insanity that came with man's ability to harness nature for his own whims.

The darkness of the subterranean room felt heavy and oppressive. The floor trembled slightly. The pungent smell of machine oil hung in the air. I felt a measure of motion sickness. I moved closer to my friend... carefully... quietly as though I did not want to draw the machines' attention to my presence in this room. I could see she was opening another door in the corner of the room. She was fiddling around for the light. I walked a little closer and could see a small, narrow space on the other side of the door. It couldn't've been bigger than a square foot or so. Hanging on the far wall was an electric showerhead – it didn't seem real. I felt as though I'd been transported back into the 1930s or 40s, I raised my head and looked more closely at the device fixed to the wall. Although I had wanted to shower for longer than I had ever done, I knew that I couldn't remain there for too long...

I had never had a shower in which I felt so anxious, so deeply worried.

In this underground pit, I showered. And as the water ran over me, my mind grew distracted, and I forgot where I was... it was as though I were in the middle of some great galactic firefight, sandwiched between hated enemies... showering. The water gushed down, moistening my skin, cleansing it of filth... The battle started again... the heavens were shorn apart, the fires burned without end. But this dark, dusky place I was in remained sealed off from all of it. The air shuddered, and the machines' cackle continued to reverberate, its pitch growing higher and higher. The water sprayed evenly over my naked body.

As I massaged the soap into my scalp, my ear remained attentive and cued to the rumbling outside. I was on alert for... for what? Earthquakes? Wars? The dam exploding? An electrical overload? Some other disaster?

I'd never felt so unsafe in the shower before. It was like bathing next to a nuclear power reactor about to experience a meltdown...

My mind then drifted to the water itself, to its temperature and how the great machines in the adjacent room were responsible for it... this 'fresh, newly generated power' – I felt an overwhelming urge to... taste this power...

Huge amounts of water are displaced, natural habitats both above and below the dam are disrupted, some destroyed completely, the paths for millions and millions of fish are blocked, choking the life out of ecological systems. All of this for 'fresh, newly generated power'. I see the fish wishing to swim upstream to spawn, only to have their passage blocked by the dam... All they can do is stare hopelessly at this violent monstrosity in front of them... But all of this is for 'fresh, newly generated power'. All for me to have a hot shower... all for people to wash themselves clean...

All for this rotten shower... I was in this pit, this abyss... a shower in hell... wash, wash, wash... Not to wash the dirt and dust off... no... I wasn't showering to remove the dirt... I showered to wash away my sins.

...

But after I finished, after I returned to the surface, my imagination ceased to run wild, and I was back in the world I had left. My hair glistened in the sky, and my whole body felt light as a feather. I felt somewhat rueful... The shower had been soooo good.

39

IGNORANCE, POWERLESSNESS

In the first few days after we arrived here, it twice rained heavily. Once the rain stopped, a wicked wind picked up, and the temperature plummeted. We couldn't help but think that the autumn rain would soon be the winter freeze. It was quite possible we were in for a tumultuous stretch of weather. But then the sunflowers bloomed so how could we not be happy? At the same time, given the weather, wasn't a measure of dismay unavoidable?

None of us could believe it when half a month later the temperature rose and the weather grew warm once again. Our autumn layer of clothes was no longer needed in the heat of the afternoon. There were even mosquitoes that were awakened from their winter slumber. It was a true Indian summer. Needless to say, we were all overjoyed.

It wasn't only the lands in the south that ended up having a difficult growing season – the fields in the north near the reservoir had their fair share of trouble, too. Seeds were sown in the spring, but a month later they'd still not sprouted. This didn't bode well and suggested there was something wrong with the seeds. Uncle felt there was nothing else to do but purchase some more and sow the land once again. As a result, our plot of land didn't show any new growth for quite a while after all of our neighbours. We never caught up on them either. When their sunflowers were ready for harvest, ours hadn't yet fully blossomed. All we could do was hope and pray that the recent spell of nice, warmer weather would last as long as it could, or at least until the flowers had been fully pollinated... But what if the cold winds did return... did flowers fear the cold? If the winter winds picked up again, would they freeze the flowers and prevent them from producing seeds?

Speaking of farming, all things considered, it should be the most dependable of hardworking activities a human can do. I mean... the work is what it is... in spring you sow seeds, in the autumn you harvest them. It's true... the work could be somewhat exhausting, but I think it was more monotonous than anything else.

But nature is beyond anyone's ability to control, and any attempt to do so entails a degree of risk, an element of chance – a gamble, no matter what one may think. Over the weather, over water, over whatever disaster might lurk just over the horizon, farming means relying on heaven for food on one's plate. No matter how we might seem to change things, or try to, there is no means by which the fate of putting seeds into the ground can be changed. A mulch could be prepared to help insulate vulnerable seeds, keep them warm, and maintain the moisture of the soil. Weed killer and pesticides could be used; fertiliser, too. Anything and everything could be done to give the seeds and sprouts all that they needed. The very earth they were planted in could be transformed. The rivers and waterways could have their courses altered, even in the remotest, most isolated places. Canals and irrigation ditches could be cut into the land... But none of that really mattered... For thousands upon thousands of years, it had been the same and would continue to be so... Life survived by chance.

An unexpected hailstone onslaught could destroy everything. A summer short on rain could wipe out a harvest. Farmers were little more than passengers on a merciless sea, afloat without a rudder, drifting across the four seasons with little more than hope that things would work out. The life of a farmer, of all farmers, is immersed in that space between heaven and earth, between what the land provides or swallows, and what the sky takes or gives;

everything is tied up to the well-being and growth of the crop they've put into the ground. Their work is open to the world, shackled to the blossoming of a single flower or a new leaf that dares to face the sun.

I am ignorant of all of this and more. I used to walk over this broad, vast and wide-open land and not pay it any attention. I used to feel no connection with it. I would quietly admire, be drunk on appreciating the earth and what man had done upon it. I would be deeply moved by man's power and ambition. At that time, I simply assumed that nature's bounty would always replenish itself... It would for evermore be there, like the crops that would grow and wait for us to pull them from the ground, like the animals that would continue to be vigorous and strong, the bumper harvests dependent only on our hard work... I was complete in this belief... and thus forever far removed from nature.

I bought my veg in the city, and it was always neatly wrapped and presented. I ate at restaurants, the dishes always overflowing. This seemed to be just how things were, how they had always been. Three meals a day... a sort of blackmail, I suppose, to keep this weak and frail bag of bones and flesh going... It was clear to me a single bowl would do it, but I had to have two at least.

Such ridiculousness... What I thought about, the sorrows and bitterness I supposedly experienced... the laughable dignity I thought I possessed – it was as though I thought their lives were solely for me, that they flourished for my benefit, that I was doing what I could for them to stand strong... to exist... to be.

It was like I lived in a bubble and had these extravagant hopes and desires that life could last for... for longer... forever... that it all just made... sense.

But now... face to face with the intimate connection between these fields and myself, there was nothing I could say... no power I could exert. I could only praise it with every fibre of my being, admire the new growth as it pushed up through the ground, eulogise the bumper harvest gifted by the land. Even a handful of desert sand was worthy of praise; so too a single droplet of water. I had to find an exit for this overwhelming passion that rushed through my body. Just one exit would do it. But the wilderness was tightly shut, the nearby Ulungur flowed day and night, and my praises fell on deaf ears. Nothing would appease my guilty conscience, nor soothe my panicky heart.

There was no peace for me. It wouldn't matter how remote, how isolated, how quiet the place might be – my heart would know no peace, no tranquillity. I am clamour. I am avarice. I am not part of this world in front of me. I am not compatible with it. Grass grows upon the sky. Reptiles spend the day in pursuit of the sun. Night belongs to the moon. Wind passes through the rivers. Rain turns ice-cold to fall like shooting stars. But only me... I am crude and simple, confined and trapped in this insignificant form. A great sorrow fermented inside me, but not a single tear ran down my cheek. My weaknesses were on full display. I was the petulant child stamping my feet for attention, a clown putting on a show in the hopes that someone would watch. But no one did. Nature turned a deaf ear to tantrum. I've spoken before... lamented many times my loneliness. I've also spoken of the many kinds of loneliness experienced by countless numbers of people. But the more I say about this, the more embarrassed I feel. I stand alone on the earth, unable to bring the show to an end.

40

VARIOUS NAMES

We'd already met the director of the hydro plant, Revolutionary Bekmyhamet, who'd been around once for dinner. Afterwards, we met another man bearing the same surname. He was not a member of the administrative staff like the former, but a simple worker. His name was no less impressive, or any less unique. Liberatory Bekmyhamet was the name given to him by his parents, and like his fellow Kazakh, it bore the mark of when he was born, which was of great interest I must say. That interest also led to a great many discussions. In fact, I'd come to know quite a few men named after the Revolution. All were Kazakhs, too. And all were born during the Cultural Revolution.

Now, if you had several boys called 'Revolutionary' then you ought to have others called 'Cultural'. Yes?

If we were to talk about sisters and daughters, well, they'd still be given 'Revolutionary' as a name, but 'Gyuli' would be added to the end instead of 'Bekmyhamet'. The former, like the latter, was common in Kazakh, with 'Bekmyhamet' being for boys, and 'Gyuli' being for girls. 'Gyuli' also meant 'flower', so I suppose it was more appropriate... That said, 'Bekmyhamet' was occasionally used for girls – one of my good friends had told me this. She'd known another Kazakh girl, a young woman actually, whose name had been 'Bekmyhamet Zhadan'... or 'Bekmyhamet Bomb'... Her brother was 'Bekmyhamet Tank'... Their younger brother was 'Bekmyhamet Rocket'... Truth.

An explosive family.

But given the circumstances at that time and the enflamed passions of most of the population, I suppose it's not totally surprising. Even the herdsmen way out here had not been immune to the great upheavals happening thousands of kilometres away.

I also knew another 'Bekmyhamet'. 'Labour' was his first name. Compared with the other names, I imagine his seems rather dull. There was a 'Worker Bekmyhamet', too. All these names – 'Labour', 'Worker', 'Revolutionary'... 'Bomb' – were Chinese, not Kazakh. They weren't used as transliterations for Kazakh names, nor, I think, were they used for their meanings (at least I hope not). No, I figured they were used somewhat indiscriminately... the first exposure to Chinese many of these Kazakhs had... that is... these were the words they kept hearing over and over during that time, even if they didn't really understand what they meant. Being so far removed from the cities, they just thought... probably... that they were good Chinese names... maybe...

The legacy of Chinese names was pronounced throughout the region, in fact. Uncle had a relative whose name was 'Rectify', which was in reference to the 'Rectify the Class Ranks' campaign. I'd also heard people being called 'Platoon'. In most cases, they'd been born during the launch of the Household or Contract responsibility system in and around 1979. If a neighbour had a child not long after, they'd end up with a name like 'Do it Yourself', which I suppose made sense in that if a platoon was divided up, people would have to work on their own... right?

Eh... I think the only thing that can be said about this naming... tradition... such as it was, was that the parents were far too nonchalant about the whole thing.

All that said, when it came to Mum choosing my name, well, that was an entirely different story. She was deliberate; she racked her brains over and over, flipped through countless dictionaries.

She wanted a name no one else had. She wanted something incomparable for me...

The result? I ended up with Li Juan.

When I lived out on the grazing fields, I heard of an old man's name... well, I forget the name, actually, but I remember if you translated it into Chinese it meant 'rolling pin'. Another was named 'Number Six Moneybags'. I never learned if there was a 'Number Five'. These two names had nothing to do with the periods in which they were born, but they were interesting nonetheless. I must say... the more I talked about this, the more excited I got. We ended up taking turns sharing fascinating stories about what we'd heard and seen throughout the area.

There was this one family... they had five sons, each named accordingly: 'First Zhan', 'Second Zhan', 'Third Zhan', 'Fourth Zhan' and... you guessed it... 'Fifth Zhan'. I'm not sure why they chose these names, beyond the obvious, but there was a rhythm to calling them out. Another family had three sons whom they called terms related to doors. I imagine their home was quite difficult for a thief to break in to.

I even heard of another three sons who were named 'Branches', 'Bark' and 'Leaves'. Two sisters' names followed a similar pattern: one was called 'Gold', the other 'Silver'. When I heard their names, I couldn't escape the image of a sparkling, shiny home.

Mum was close to another family who had similarly unique names for their children. Their oldest was born on the same day a car was first seen in their village. Now, in those days, automobiles were a rare sight, and many had never even seen one before. Unsurprisingly, their first child was named after the... event... 'Che Lai' or 'Car's Come'... When their second was born, another car had come through the town, but this one had stopped. Yes... they did... 'Che Ting'... 'Car's Stopped' was given as the child's name... The third... well, he nearly popped out while she was on her way into town, hence his name, 'Che Zhan'... 'Bus Stop'... When the fourth was due, times had moved on, and cars and buses were no longer a rare sight. But telephones were. On the day his daughter came, the mayor of the town had instructed him to head to the main offices to receive a telephone call. After he'd done that and returned home to see his new child, he gave her the name 'Telephone'...

After forty or fifty years, people had become so accustomed to her name that they didn't think anything of it. Only Mum, who wasn't around all that much, thought the name strange. Each time she heard it, she couldn't help but chuckle.

I also knew an older man – not too old, about my uncle's age – whose name was 'Donkey's Head'... All right... I don't know if the name was due to the way the man looked or because of his perceived intelligence... or lack thereof... A lady had the name 'Diligence' – I suppose her name was suggestive of the expectation her parents put on her. Then there was 'Bulky', born during a period of material scarcity... The child was the... the largest item they had... and thus the most presentable... A son, after all, was cause to be happy in any case... a large boy, well, even more so... which meant his name had to reflect that.

There was a slew of other names, too, and while their meanings may not have always been plain, they were special in their way nonetheless: 'Noodles' – well, this was kind of a tired, used-before type of name... When people tried to say it, they often would stop halfway...

There was 'Fork'... yes... just the one word. A pair of girls named 'Qiong Jin' and 'Qiong Kuai', or 'Fine Jade Towel' and 'Fine Jade Cloth'. 'Ningning' was another name I heard, or 'Twist'... which resulted in her dad being called 'Baba Twist'.

Finally, I must mention 'Great Red Flower'. She was a worker we employed from time to time. Mum and I were forever curious about the three words in her name. Had they been chosen for their meaning, or for the way they sounded? Was it a nickname or her actual name?

41

GREAT RED FLOWER

Early in the morning, before I was even out of bed, Great Red Flower had already arrived. I remember she pushed open the door and walked straight up to my bed. She then fished out a wooden stool and plopped herself down atop it, her face not far from mine. Her position was set as though she were about to do battle – Great Red Flower let loose an unceasing torrent of invective and complaint. The first words were about her son's daughter who was due to start school and how they didn't have nearly enough money to pay her fees... Then she switched topics to her younger brother who was ill and who had been thinking about heading to the county capital for tests... Unfortunately, they only had enough money for a one-way ticket... Then she complained about her family's livestock, or lack thereof, for they had no cattle, no sheep, no nothing... they didn't even have land of their own to till. I thought to try and get a word in edgeways, to tell her that although she mightn't have land, she was able to go out and work and earn money for rent at least... but I couldn't, and she only cried and wailed some more... There wasn't a town fifty kilometres in either direction that would allow her to buy on credit...

There was nothing I could do. I pulled my legs up under me and wrapped my quilt tightly around my frame so that only my head was exposed. Then I sat patiently and waited for her to finish her diatribe. The only reason she came was to grumble and curse her situation. Once done, she left. She didn't have a problem with me.

Great Red Flower was about fifty years old... probably. Her hair was fully white. Her voice was loud and intimidating. The arch of her nose was high, and she was just less than two metres tall. Her arms and legs were rough and coarse. By any measure, she was a stocky, tough-looking, mannish kind of woman. She was also a permanent fixture in these parts.

It was a pity, then, that such an imposing figure meant her choice in clothing was rather limited. Indeed, she often appeared more comical than anything else. A sleeveless garment three sizes too small, her bellybutton uncovered for all to see; a cheongsam that resembled more a cleaning rag, so long it bunched up on the top of her feet.

She was unlike any of the other Kazakh women for she never wore a petticoat. The result of this... choice (?) was that her cheongsam constantly ran in between her butt cheeks, creating a most unappealing image – in fact, each time I happened to see her strolling like this, well, it was hard not to reach over and try and help her out, to pull the cheongsam free.

To exacerbate things even further, she never wore socks, but instead adorned her feet with a pair of old, worn-out men's sandals. The filth that had gathered under her overgrown toenails looked fierce and malevolent.

But I suppose when you're toiling away all day, exhausted and generally overworked, it's understandable that things like this would fly under the radar. It's just that, well, Great Red Flower seemed to be taking this to the extreme.

Before we moved up here, my uncle had spent quite a long period of time in the same town as Great Red Flower. Amongst Kazakhs in the area, it was a custom that outsiders, especially a single Chinese man, should not be cooking his evening meals alone. Consequently, Uncle enjoyed the privilege of going from door to door, from meal to meal. Normally, this would result in him visiting houses more than once – he'd do a round, as it were, and start back over. But he only ever went to Great Red Flower's house the one time. Once, he said, was enough, and he didn't dare go a second time.

There's really nothing else to say about it... not really... I mean, according to Uncle, even the butter she had at her place struck fear into him, into any visitor for that matter, for it was far more reddish than yellow and looked as if it'd been left out in a hot summer more than once... try ten times. Uncle described it as being soft and watery, and covered with flies. There were dead ones buried in it, and some, still not dead, struggling mightily to free themselves. Going to this house again... well... it wasn't worth it, Uncle said.

A single Chinese out in the world trying to make a living, well, there was that I suppose. But Great Red Flower's house, according to Uncle, was filled with what seemed like the same sort of men. When dinnertime came, she would actually step outside, look in all directions to find the first home that had a chimney lit, and then send her children off running towards it.

They would eat whatever their neighbours were cooking; beggars, after all, shouldn't be choosers. But if, on the other hand, they weren't all that forthcoming, then she'd have cause to fly into a rage.

That is to say, for instance, if there was dried meat hanging above the stove, but only noodles boiling away in a pot just under them, well, she wouldn't hesitate to grab the meat, soften it up, and throw the whole lot into the soup... to her mind, they shouldn't skimp on what they had...

Those times she showed up at our yurt, she'd always come in bold as anything, survey the scene, and then lock sights onto her target. Then she'd gesture towards the bed and exclaim bluntly what it was she wanted. "The tomato! Give us one!"

I could only acquiesce, rush over and grab one, and then give it to her.

"A bigger one... come on now, do us right!"

I made no effort to resist, and she accepted the larger tomato without another word. She didn't leave, however, but instead walked over to the bed, scanned it for a minute as though she were unsure of its stability, and then sat down to begin munching on the fruit I'd given her. Once finished, her eyes again surveyed the yurt.

"Where's your mum?"

"Not here."

"And your dad?"

"Not here either... Do you need them for anything?"

"Nah..." That was all she said before lifting her girth from the bed as solemnly and dignified as she could, and then departing.

If it hadn't been for the tomato plant hanging there when she first arrived, there was no telling what might've happened.

When it came to work, however, Great Red Flower was certainly worthy of praise. She was unrivalled out in the fields, chopping four strips of sunflowers with such precision and skill I could only hope to match. In truth, it was extremely difficult for me to even keep half her pace. What's more, not only would she be swinging her blade and cutting the sunflowers down, she would also at the same time be cracking shells and devouring the seeds. She was a true marvel.

Unsurprisingly, when harvest season rolled around, the busiest time of year for farmers, Great Red Flower's services were in high demand. This meant, or at least it should've, that this was the most important time of year for her family, a chance to make a fair bit of coin in a relatively short period of time. Well... the only thing was, it didn't seem that way. I mean, there was very little change in her family's routine. They still showed up at other people's homes much as they had always done. Great Red Flower would still come late to work on most days, and she would leave early in the evenings, too. What's more, she still took her siestas in the afternoons... a good two hours at least... time for whiling away, sharing gossip or just shooting the breeze... just as she always did... In a word... amazing.

Of course, we hired Great Red Flower for the busy season – how could we not? Unfortunately for our neighbours, they were the ones who felt the most grief at her presence. (I'm talking here of the workers at the hydro plant.)

My whole family were Chinese, which meant it wasn't always convenient for us to try and follow Islamic rules regarding what was okay to eat and what wasn't. To further complicate matters, or maybe to make them more straightforward, our plot of land was a tad more remote than most other ones in the area; the terrain was rather rough, too. What this meant was that there wasn't really anywhere convenient for us to prepare snacks for our workers, and as a result, most of them brought their own food. So I guess that made things a little simpler for us. That is until we hired Great Red Flower. She wouldn't bring her own meals and snacks; instead, she'd bring just a bowl and her chopsticks.

How does this connect to the hydro plant workers? Well, I'm getting to that.

Because we didn't prepare food, and because Great Red Flower wouldn't bring any of her own, while she worked for us she would take her meals at the hydro plant's canteen, which, luckily, prepared halal food...

I didn't really know what kind of freeloaders Great Red Flower and her family were when it came to getting a meal, but they seemed to know the exact mealtimes at the canteen and would be there accordingly when the rest of the hydro plant workers went to eat. Not long after they started doing this, I would hear the canteen attendant, a woman by the name of Shana, yell out that they weren't to be allowed in, that there wasn't enough food for Great Red Flower and her family, that there were still workers who hadn't yet arrived and so they certainly couldn't allow non-employees to eat up all of the food. She refused to go along with this explanation, and later on I heard a shouting match between Great Red Flower and the director of the hydro plant, who was yelling at her not to return on the next day, nor any day thereafter... According to him, she'd already had much more than she should've. Perhaps out of character... I don't know... but Great Red Flower didn't respond as expected. No... she was quiet instead and chose to just put her head down, circle the canteen table, and continue doing what she had already been doing.

Let me tell you... I wasn't moved by Great Red Flower's brazenness. No... I was more moved by everybody else's ability to put up with her.

There's more to say about Great Red Flower. Indeed... a life filled with its fair share of hardships and vexations is bound to have more stories, and a need to seek small pleasures and happiness wherever it can. That's why, I imagine, they did what they did. On the two busiest days of the harvest season, Great Red Flower and her entire family would excuse themselves from work. The reason? Well, on the second of these two days off, about a hundred kilometres or so away, there would be a grand performance of aqyn singers, along with physical feats and challenges, and dance, too. The aqyn singers were especially entertaining, a mixture of improvised verse and song, usually accompanied by Kazakh lutes called dombyras, and often about life on the plains.

Needless to say, this was a most unwelcome time for us farmers and caused us no small amount of consternation – after all, how in hell were we to get extra workers to finish off the job when it was nearly complete, and yet had the hardest bit left? In addition to the stress we already felt, the arrival of the herdsmen and their flocks from the south made things even worse, for before they could cross the Ulungur we had to have our sunflowers cut and dried – otherwise, the herds would walk over and destroy everything. A whole summer's worth of work would be ruined, and we'd have nothing to show for it.

What a mad rush we were in! Of course, Mum cursed a blue streak, even though it would have no effect. She also offered increased wages for anyone who would come at the last minute. This didn't work either. She gritted her teeth hard and spat. "You should all die poor, you bastards! You've got a little bit of cash, huh, and you don't want more... bloody freaks!"

This was her usual refrain. After all, she'd called me a freak more than once before, so I was familiar with her complaints. But I tried nevertheless to calm Mum down. I told her there wasn't much point in getting all fussed about it – they were already poor enough, they had to enjoy what small pleasures they could, I told her, and if they missed the aqyn performance, well, what would be the point of it all... Why work so hard if there was no reward? My words seemed to have the desired effect. Mum, at least, thought they made some sense, and she ceased her tirade.

Of course, that meant the only option left for us was to complete the work on our own. This meant the next two days were spent out in the fields even before the sun came up, and long after it went down. It was so dark that you couldn't even see your fingers in front of you. And was it ever tiring... exhausting... We were completely knackered... like a burned-out monkey too gassed to do anything further... but we finished the job... before the herds needed to cross the Ulungur.

We'd worked unendingly for a week, and our hands had paid the price. Torn, sore, hurting... it was hard to even pick up our chopsticks at the dinner table. But we did save four hundred yuan by doing the work ourselves... There was that...

When I thought about Great Red Flower again and the calmness with which she completed her work, well, I had to admire her just a little more, even if I still grumbled about her leaving us in the lurch.

Great Red Flower's appearance at the aqyn performance was nothing like the image she wore while out in the sunflower fields. She'd changed from top to toe; it was really quite refreshing. I'd seen her once in Akehala – at the market I think it was. She had makeup on and looked nothing like the woman we'd grown accustomed to seeing on the plains. She was wearing a gold, velvet skirt adorned with heavy layers of brightly coloured flowers. The necklace she had on had beads as big as quail eggs. A purple shawl was over her shoulders, and a silver hairpin glistened on the top of her head. Her face was the colour of snow, her eyebrows jet-black. She was also wearing boots, of all things, well-polished, too! In Mum's words, the boots were so slick that ants would need walking sticks just to climb on.

In truth, dressing up to try and show off usually results in the person looking a little tacky – vulgar even. But this was not the case with Great Red Flower. She was all decked out, for sure, but she still looked impressive, still carried herself in that same manner as when she was out on the fields. Despite the clothes and makeup, she was still Great Red Flower. I mean, she was a big woman, mannish in a way, there's no discounting that, but the makeup just made her more impressive. When she appeared as she did at the performance, walking forward with great strides, holding in each hand a child in brightly coloured clothes, she was absolutely mesmerising. There was no way anyone's attention could be diverted to anything else.

Although I never really figured out why she was called 'Great Red Flower', I couldn't think of another name that would suit her so well! And I don't know why it did... Maybe it just... did... 'Great Red Flower' – a good name... yes, 'Great Red Flower'!

42

HIRED HANDS

The sunflowers were ripe. The very yellow petals were already falling down, if only one at a time. The dark seeds were nearly overwhelming the heart of the flower. The flowers were so heavy in fact that the stems slumped noticeably towards the ground. We had to wait, however, for their heads to turn to the sky. They had to look at the sun, to feel its warmth. They had to be tanned, too, dried under the sun's rays so that the seeds would easily fall to the ground at the slightest touch. Then and only then would we cut the sunflowers down.

Each person went out into the fields holding a cleaver. Our left hands would take hold of the stalks while our right hands wielded the blade and the flowers fell. The remaining stalks also had to be cut and properly prepared. Normally we cut at an angle, that way the remaining stem could still absorb water. The pieces shorn off of the flower would be about a metre or so long. With these, we could place the cut flowers on top of them, which made it easier to carry the crop out of the field. The remaining stems would either be torn up from the ground or beaten down to fertilise the next rotation of sunflower plants. It sounds kind of complicated, but in truth it was just a swoosh of the blade and then a few more quick movements. It only took a few seconds for each flower. It couldn't really be considered that physically hard, either. I mean, it didn't take that much power.

I swung my knife as vigorously as I could, slicing through the air before striking the flower. Compared to everyone else, I was keeping pace, which, for a few minutes of work, gave me quite the sense of accomplishment. After several mu cut, however, my arm began to grow stiff and I could feel a soreness in my shoulder. My waist was starting to hurt, too, and, in truth, I was beginning to feel rather concerned over my general health and well-being. By the following day, I felt as though I'd aged years.

Once the large sunflower discs were thoroughly dried, we could complete the harvest. This was rather easy to do, for all it took was to place the large sunflowers, or rather what we could call their face, the petals and the heart where the seeds grew, into bags and then drag them across the ground. Next, the flowers had to be beaten. To do this, they'd be placed upon a large piece of plastic tarpaulin. The men and women responsible for carrying out this task all held smallish pieces of wood in their hands – rolling pins, essentially – which were to be used on the sunflowers. They'd continue striking the plants and rolling their sticks over them until all of the seeds were freed. This wasn't exactly hard work, but it was tiresome nonetheless.

Each time it came to doing this, I remember I started with great vigour, sparing no effort whatsoever. I also remember cursing to myself, wondering why in hell we had planted so many bloody sunflowers. I had to rejoice, too, grateful that we hadn't planted five hundred mu!

Sometime later, I happened to watch a video. It showed a farmer... somewhere... who had taken his bicycle and flipped it upside down so that the wheels faced the sky. He then used one hand to pedal the bike, and in his other hand he held a sunflower close to the spinning wheel... "Waaaa!" Amazing! The sunflower seeds flew in every which direction, and before long the entire face had been scraped clean.

This invention was enough to make you sing... or cry! If only I'd seen the video a few years earlier...

It was during this kind of work that I felt myself growing older. Whether or not I was actually ageing wasn't really the issue. I just felt increasingly old, especially at the end of the day when I was so exhausted I couldn't even eat. I remember the wind blew fiercely, too, on those days. It whistled and swirled around us, buffeting, assaulting us without mercy; it felt like the whole world was roaring up in some kind of protest against us. I pulled the shawl I was wearing tighter around my shoulders and neck and continued to toil. In front of me, there was a small mountain of sunflowers. Behind me, there was another small mountain, but this one was of carcasses – sunflowers pared of their seeds – which lay scattered around me.

I worked robotically, without feeling the blisters all across my hands. What was the saying? 'Dripping water penetrates the stone'... Why couldn't I get that out of my mind? I imagine the amount of effort I put into this work over those two days was, well, quite a bit... I reckoned I'd have little difficulty laying the foundation of a building on my own... But why was I working alone? Where in hell were Mum and Uncle?

I found out later that Uncle was busy looking for more workers. Mum, on the other hand, had returned to Akehala to open her store... She had to find some way to make money to pay our workers' wages...

The other hired hands fulfilled other short-term jobs much like Great Red Flower had done, and even if there was some dissatisfaction, they were able to offset the loss of Great Red Flower and allow us to complete the work that needed doing. Of course, there weren't a great number of seasonal workers around, nor were there, in fact, a great number of seasonal jobs to begin with. I don't know why since the salaries for temp work had increased over the last two years, but there were fewer and fewer workers around. Maybe it was a case of more and more new land being opened up for cultivation? More land, yes, but from beginning to end the labour force had remained the same.

Most of the seasonal workers came from the nearby villages. But most of them, out here in the wilderness, as remote as we were, weren't exactly booming and bustling towns filled with loads of people. What's more, in the summer, most of the capable workers would follow the herds of sheep north with the rest of the herdsmen. It was straightforward work, after all. As a result, most households had only one or two people left to look after their homes, and these people ended up being busy taking care of their own pastureland.

The wealthier farmers, who had much more land to till, would hire workers from the county city when the busy season rolled around. But for us small-time farmers responsible for only a couple of hundred mu, well, the prospects of hiring workers from the city was something that would never happen. The remoteness of where we were didn't help matters either, for the nearest city was well over a hundred kilometres away. Now... if we were to hire people from the city, not only would we have to pay for their transportation and their food, but we'd also have to make arrangements for where they could sleep – a dormitory or something – which was a lot easier said than done, to say nothing of how much it would cost.

Most of the time, farming sunflowers meant a lot of idle time spent sitting around, waiting. But when the busy seasons started, they started. No one got angry about it – we were probably happier just to have something to do, even if it would be hard.

Sowing seeds, watering them, spreading fertiliser, spraying pesticides, pruning, harvesting, these were all labour-intensive jobs... and they all had to be completed in short periods of time – a delay of but even a few days could greatly impact how well the plants would grow and what the harvests would be like.

As it happened, the tens of thousands of mu of sunflower seeds were more or less on the same cycle. That meant when we were busy, so was everyone else. When we were looking to hire temporary workers, all our neighbours were, too. Conflict was unavoidable; we were each trying to outmanoeuvre the other, undermine the other for our own benefit, and increase the salaries we offered, all in the hope of getting the workers we needed.

It was no wonder Mum and my uncle always felt miserable at these times.

During one such harvest season, we hired a relatively young boy to work for us. In the afternoons, he'd play around with his keychain and shoot the breeze with Uncle. The chain for his keys had a small piece of plastic bearing the image of some celebrity attached to it.

"Who's that there, huh? Your brother?"

"That's Yao Ming! You know... he played in the NBA." His face betrayed the adoration he had for the former basketball star.

"Can he harvest sunflowers? Whaddya think?"

"I told you he was in the NBA... That's basketball... in America... He were a star you know!"

"A star?"

"He was 2.2 metres tall!"

"Ring him then, eh. Tell 'im we've got work for him... eighty yuan a day."

In the past, my work involved cooking the meals, washing the laundry, feeding the chickens and pulling up weeds in the fields... that probably accounted for half of everything I did. But once we started experiencing labour shortages, my work increased tenfold; I had to do all of the usual chores, and go out into the fields, too.

Mum felt the pain of this situation as well. She rued the lack of mechanisation out in the fields, or rather the lack of any effort on the part of the authorities to make such mechanisation possible. "We're going backwards in time!" she would shout to no one in particular. "We're no better off than we were thirty years ago! Machines... ha! I don't see them here!"

She wasn't wrong in what she said, I guess. After all, in the past she'd been part of a peasants' military brigade, an agricultural technician, and she'd been quite accomplished at it, too. She remembered the promise of the new agriculture... glorious memories of her youth, I suppose you could say.

Mechanisation would of course increase output, and it was probably more reliable. I'd even heard that some people considered it to be more dignified... but I think she missed an important point... The lack of mechanisation out here meant that she could still actually till the land and sow her seeds... That wouldn't necessarily be the case if the area had become an industrialised farming area. Maybe she thought this way because she was quickly running out of cash to pay the few seasonal workers we had... Machines, I suppose, don't need to be paid... Perhaps that's why she dared to think in this way... I'm not sure... But think about it... Would she have enough cash to hire a plane to spray pesticides? Would it even be necessary? I mean, we had only a hundred mu... by the time a plane reached the right altitude, it would have passed by our farmland and ended up spraying our neighbours, too. How would we benefit from that?

WAITING

It's true, when we needed additional help most, we couldn't find any workers to hire. I'd always thought farming was about putting in the effort, and that it just needed manpower. I'd never once thought it needed investments of money, too. Mulch and fertilisers, pesticides and honeybees, all of these things required cold hard cash. Right from the beginning when the soil was first tilled and seeds planted, to the pruning, the cutting, the removal of seeds, we needed hired hands for all of this, and that meant spending money. That's why, by the time it came to harvesting the sunflowers, Mum was flat out broke. And everybody knew you couldn't squeeze blood from a turnip.

Mum did whatever she could to make sure she had enough money to cover her costs, but it often never worked. I remember once, before the planting season began, she sold off a newly built house to ensure she had cash reserves. We were supposed to live in the new place but ended up moving into a dormitory that was adjacent to it. At that time, I was also bringing in a little bit of cash, and I put all of it towards Mum's enterprise. But the water level in the bottle never seemed to increase, and the crow's beak would never reach it.

If we hired a long-term worker, well, we could fall behind in our payment of wages by a month or two, and that would be all right. But a short-term worker? No way. Money had to be paid straight away. There was no flexibility whatsoever, and if we tried, we'd simply not be able to hire anyone in the first place. A hundred and ten yuan was the usual wage, and if we tried to give it on future credit, they'd be none too pleased, and we really couldn't blame them.

Mum did, however, hire a long-term worker, a young Kazakh boy. After a month of toiling away carrying basket after basket, the boy had not learned anything about advanced farming techniques using technology. He was a Muslim, too, which meant meals were no longer always easy and straightforward. I suppose it was good we didn't eat pork, which wasn't halal in any case, but for kids who grew up on milk tea and who now had to eat porridge without it, well, that wasn't really fair now, was it? We also didn't have that much land to manage. Now, having a long-term hired hand made things easier for Mum, especially during the busy season, but when it wasn't busy, there was nothing for him to do, and the non-busy season was a helluva lot longer than the busy one.

Once Mum did the calculations, there was little choice but to let the hired hand go.

Ironically perhaps, I don't know, but he was happy about his dismissal.

That was the last time Mum ever hired a long-term worker. It was also after this that she would clench her teeth whenever the busy season rolled around – really grind them, too. She endured this, at first, but as more time passed and the work didn't get any easier, it became harder and harder for her to make it through. Ultimately, she relented and sought to hire temporary workers. She had to spend the money, even though she loathed doing so. It was also around this time that her mind turned to memories of her former small convenience store.

Akehala was a small town with a small population. At the centre of the town, there were quite a few little shops selling mostly basic groceries. There was only one city wholesaler who bothered to come to Akehala, however, which meant each shop carried the same items. Our family store had been rather small, and we didn't have a great number of things in it to begin with, which was, I suppose, the reason why we hadn't gone out of business. That, and Mum's competitive spirit that wouldn't allow her to fail – at least, that's a sweet way of putting it.

That said, because of Mum's efforts to succeed at farming, the shop hadn't been opened in more than half a year, which also meant no new items had been put on its shelves for at least that long. If she were to unshutter the doors, well, it was certain business wouldn't immediately boom. Still, she wanted to try nonetheless.

After pollination, there was nothing to do but wait for the seeds and plants to mature. Mum decided to take advantage of the free time, such as it was, and return to Akehala. She sped off one morning on her motorcycle and didn't return until the sky had grown pitch-black. The happiness in her voice made us forget the lateness of her return. She'd reopened the shop, and in half a day's business she'd made eighty yuan! The exact amount needed for a day's work on the farm.

I've mentioned before how most towns empty in the summer. This meant there weren't a great deal of items to be bought in Akehala, so the fact she'd been able to make eighty yuan was pretty good indeed. Eighty yuan for dusty items on a shelf, not bad... I wondered how much more she could make. "How far is it to drive back and forth? How much did you spend on petrol for the trip?"

Mum counted on her fingers before answering my query. "It's all right! If I were to sell but thirty yuan of goods I'd still make a profit."

That was the start of it. Every chance she had thereafter she went into Akehala and opened the store doors. Her gumption, her last resort, as it were, seemed to be worth it.

Each day she'd head off to her store just after the sun came up and wouldn't return until it had already set over the horizon. Each day she'd make fifty-plus yuan or more. On bad days, she'd still haul in twenty or thirty. On one particularly good day, she sold nearly two hundred yuan worth of goods. Needless to say, she was over the moon and even broke out into song that night.

"If I could get a couple of more days making that kind of money, well then, I could take the next couple of days after that off." She didn't make a penny the two following days. The happiness she'd felt had been quickly cancelled out.

She complained to no one in particular: "What a blasted waste... these past two days... If only I'd known, I'd've stayed at home... I could've helped Juan in the fields at least."

Eh? What did she say – 'help' me with the work in the fields?

How did that work become 'mine'?

Despite her vitriolic grumbling, on the following day she packed a bit of food, two thick fried pancakes, bundled herself up nice and warm, and then braved the biting wind to head back into town. She had to keep trying her luck with the store.

You know... the hardest part for Mum wasn't the travel back and forth; the kilometres meant very little to her. It was the battle of wits – the struggle between shopkeeper and customer – that Mum found most challenging. And the business grew more and more difficult as the year went on. Akehala was a stopping point at best, a town located on the shepherds' route. This meant the wealth followed the herds. It was also the reason why the town was virtually deserted in the summer and why, for those who remained, life was so hard and money so tight. The shortness of cash also meant that when they did go shopping, they tried to get as much as they could for as little as possible, like the person who squeezes the last bit of toothpaste out of the tube before even considering buying another.

It was not uncommon to see...

"That works... yes... I'll say it again – twenty yuan... Can you pack these trousers up for me."

"Twenty yuan? You're talking nonsense, surely. Twenty yuan for a pair of trousers?"

"Twenty-one then."

"I can't sell for less than twenty-nine."

"Twenty-three! That's it, no more."

"Twenty-eight. Take it or leave it... It's up to you... I'm not bothered either way."

"All right, all right... How about twenty-three yuan and fifty mao? C'mon, we're friends aren't we?"

"Friends have to eat, don't they?"

"Okay... okay... Twenty-three and eight..."

At that point, Mum would usually take her ruler and proceed to strike the customer with it.

To get to Akehala from the hydro station meant going straight along the provincial highway until you reached it; there were no turns, no forks, just straight road. It was a good road, too – very few potholes and, for the most part, level. There weren't many vehicles on it either, which meant most drivers felt no hesitation in flooring it. *Zoom... zoom...* was the most frequent sound heard; there were quite a few accidents as well.

At the same time, it should be mentioned that the herdsmen who lived in the villages alongside the road weren't always circumspect about how they managed their flocks. It was thus not uncommon for whole herds to be up on the road, congregating close together and blocking any means through. There were even times when the cattle would squat down on the road and use it as their bed. They were completely unbothered by any vehicles that showed up – even blaring horns were of no use. All that the drivers could do was stop, cut the ignition, and then get out and use their feet to kick at the rears of the cattle. Either that or use a stick to rap across their bellies and get them to stir. And even then, the animals would only do so reluctantly, hesitantly, begrudgingly. By the afternoon, the cattle would fill the road in both directions once again.

To make matters worse, there were no street lights along the highway, which made it rather difficult to see the cows at night, even with the car or bus lights turned on. Mum and Uncle had already had an incident with the cattle in the past. It was at night while they were on their motorbike. They were going quite fast and came upon a black cow in the middle of the road before they could do very little about it. They crashed into the creature, and the bike went flying, as did Mum and Uncle. Fortunately, they were both wearing helmets, so they ended up with scrapes and bruises rather than worse injuries. They did have to hobble around for a few days, limping painfully, but they had avoided more serious harm.

And the cow?

Mum told me it got up from the accident and ran off...

Since it ran, she assumed there was very little wrong with it.

As a result, once Mum started going back and forth along the highway again, I couldn't help but be on edge and nearly scared out of my wits. My worries only got worse as she began coming home later and later each evening.

It was my responsibility to prepare the dinner, which meant I spent a great deal of time bent over the hot stove. But as the horizon darkened, as the stars appeared, my heart would grow increasingly uneasy. A few minutes later and I would be at the door peering off towards the southeast, hoping to catch sight of Mum. Should a faint sound of some vehicle happen to carry on the evening air, I would drop everything and race to the door to see if it was her. And it wasn't only me – Saihu and Chouchou would do the same.

As for these two almost feral dogs... throughout the day they'd be out and about, going crazy about this or that, and we wouldn't see a single trace of them. But when the sun set, they'd be back. Always. They'd sit at the door, staring off to the southeast in the direction that Mum should come.

Whenever a wind picked up from the southeast, strong and fierce, Chouchou's ears would prick up, and he would stand at attention as though waiting to pounce. Saihu, for her part, would stand on her hind legs, looking as far into the distance as she could, a low, nervous howl bubbling up from inside her.

This was a feeling of worry and concern... I suppose... but there was an element of calmness to it as well. Living in complicated times, in complex environments, there are bound to be things one can manage and things that one cannot. Now... in the cities... when it comes to family and friends, even when concerns and worries arise, these are much easier to pare down, to overcome. But out in the wilderness, in this simple, quiet kind of life, those same small worries are more likely to become that much bigger. Waiting for Mum like that, I had a difficult time trying to control my thoughts, to rein them in. There was no difference between me and the two dogs. We were, all three of us, standing there in the dark, in the wind, staring into the emptiness, into the abyss that stretched out into nothingness.

Mum enjoyed riding her bike. It made her feel... alive. Speeding down the highway, hugging the turns... it was like she was living one of her dreams... competing in a rally race, soon to win it and then having every reporter hang on her every word. But if anyone brought this fantasy up, she would just curse and grumble that she was too old... and that that was all anyone would see.

But being of a certain age isn't all bad...

Mum's bike had a rather large engine, which made the vehicle quite heavy. Forget about riding it – for me, it was difficult to even hold it steady... to say nothing about pushing it... But Mum, she was brave and bold, although not reckless, not impulsive. She knew when to be cautious, and how to carry herself appropriately...

But out here in the middle of nowhere, buffeted by the endless-ness of the Gobi Desert... a great almost level plain that spread out as far as the eye could see... no trees, no people, no cars or any other vehicles... nor even a protruding mound of earth... out here... this is where Mum rode her bike... and where... where she still signalled if she chose to turn left... or right.

When I first heard about this, I laughed. "Who do you do it for, huh?"

"For no one." There was an unexpected seriousness in her tone. "It's for me... I wanna make it like second nature... everyone should signal after all."

I couldn't help but admire her... even though I kept it to myself.

She'd cursed other drivers who neglected to turn on their indi-cators. If the other driver didn't hear her invective, well, she'd increase speed and begin to chase him or her. She wouldn't relent, either, not until she pulled up alongside and shouted at the vehicle's window, berating the driver for not signalling. "How in hell can I know which way you're turning if you don't signal? You might wanna die... but the least you could do is think about others on the road!"

An amateur traffic cop. Or a weekend police fan.

But was it worth it? Did it make any difference? Mum might've known all about signalling, but she didn't understand red and green lights...

Because of Mum's renewed enterprising spirit, the days always ended with me, and the dogs, waiting. It wasn't a fun sort of waiting, either. No, it was me and the dogs peering off into the darkness, each night, later and later, looking for – hoping for – any sign of Mum's motorbike lights breaking through the blanket of night. And as the time crawled slowly by, we would long for the light, to see it coming in this direction, to see it drawing nearer and nearer, to have it grow brighter and brighter. It was at these times that I thought of Granny and how she had waited for me... on the balcony... watching for me to appear at the end of the day.

Waiting is like the root of loneliness... isn't it? I mean, the more you wait, the more the loneliness grows, the more it flourishes, swallowing up everything else until only solitude remains...

Later, much later, the motorbike light would appear, and it would snake its way closer and closer. Finally, Mum was back. The two dogs howled into the night, excited and relieved she'd returned.

In truth, the dogs had already left my side. As soon as they spied the light for her bike, they took off running in its direction, always welcoming her first. It was as though they'd been separated from Mum for fifty-plus years, or something like that – even though it was only a day.

Chouchou's hind legs were especially long, which meant he could run at great speeds. He'd make a beeline for Mum, running fast and hard like a cannon shooting into the dark. Of course, this mighty dog bounding up towards her would frighten Mum to no end, and she'd slam on her brakes, startled but also touched by Chouchou's excitement at her return. "Bloody dog! You tryin' to kill yerself?" Her curse, however, betrayed her affection.

Chouchou, of course, showed no fear. Even before she'd fully stop, he would already be jumping up as though he were trying to grapple the bike, and Mum along with it, to the ground. A second later and his great tongue would stretch out and give her the wettest of wet licks... right across her face. Mum would attempt to dodge, but she was always unsuccessful. She couldn't, after all, just let go of the handlebars and fling the bike to one side – she might hurt Chouchou... All she could do was yell out to me to grab him and pull him off. It was quite the sight.

I would oblige, of course, and throw my arms around Chouchou's broad neck and pull him back. It took a great deal to rescue her from his affections.

Saihu's affections were entirely different – much more reserved and contained. Her welcome was a plaintive cry, and a chasing about underfoot. She'd also stand on her hind legs and hop up and down against Mum's legs, acting very much like the spoilt child who wishes to be picked up. Mum would continue to curse Chouchou and at the same time coax Saihu, all while removing her helmet and overcoat.

After she stepped inside, the first thing she would do – this was her new routine – was announce how the day's business had been. "Eighty yuan again, I tell ya! Not too shabby, not too shabby at all... Another day's wages for a hired hand!"

44

DRIVING CATTLE

While waiting for the sunflowers to ripen and then to dry, Uncle spent his time searching for additional workers and doing various other odd jobs. Mum was busy going back and forth into town, earning what money she could to pay hired hands to help with the harvesting of the sunflowers. As for me... I took care of the yurt... doing household chores. I suppose, in a way, I had the easier go of it, but that's not the way I felt – to me, I was just as busy as them...

First, I had to feed the rabbits. That meant pulling grass, again... and again... and again... until I ached all over. Next, I had to catch the blasted rabbits for they were experts in breaking out of their enclosure, like criminals freeing themselves from prison. Even the really young ones could do it after only a few days away from their mums. It was quite something, actually, to see them bound over a fence that was just over sixty centimetres. Previously, I never would've dared to think this is what I would be doing – spending my waking hours chasing after damn rabbits! You have to understand, too, that these creatures were nothing if not full of life, frisky, active, and incredibly swift and agile, able to leap away from me even when I thought I had them for sure... And I was the fool vainly trying to catch them... After all, putting lightning back in a bottle isn't the easiest thing to do. To make things even more challenging, they were also rather small, so they would not only bound past me before I could grab onto them but also squirrel away into little nooks and crannies that I simply couldn't reach in to. This made it impossible for me to get them, even when I knew where they were.

I don't know... maybe I underestimated myself. I hadn't really thought about it... But after three days of chasing the little rascals, I'd learned a new skill. It didn't matter how far they might've run, all I needed to do to catch them was grab their long ears and hold on tight... Then I could bring them to... What? Justice... I suppose, for running away...

Besides feeding and chasing the rabbits, I also had to look after the chickens. You might think it would be simpler because chicken feed was more or less ready-made – a bit of bran, wheat husks mixed with a little water and that was it. The problem, however, was that we had no money... at least none to buy chicken feed, which meant my pulling up grasses in the morning took on extra importance. In the past, we'd given the chickens proper feed, but they had nothing much more than wild grasses. Of course, with fifty-plus chickens to feed, this wasn't exactly ideal...

But... these household chores were nothing compared with herding cattle. On this occasion, our sunflower fields were greatly delayed, which meant we'd not yet harvested the crop before it came time for the herdsmen to run their cattle south. In fact, we'd only just cut the flowers before the cattle started to make the passage across the river... which meant our defence of the fields started in earnest.

I should first describe how the cows ate the heads of the flowers, the great disc that we'd cut and left on the ground to dry before harvesting the seeds. One mouthful from a hungry bovine and all that remained would be a crescent-moon-shaped carcass. I suppose you'd assume the animal would continue and take a second bite, fully consuming the sunflower disc, yes? Well, you'd be wrong. The creature instead would lower its head once more, and then that dastardly mouth would proceed to make a second crescent moon.

The sunflower fields were large and deep, which meant there

weren't only one or two cows concealed in amongst it... no, there could be a whole herd hiding out inside, busily devouring our plants. I suppose they felt safe and comfortable under the flowers for there was plenty of food about, as well as cover from the sun. And none of the animals would leave, at least not until they'd filled their bellies.

Needless to say, rounding up the cattle meant having to circle the fields, all the hundred mu, repeatedly, looking for any sign of the beasts, and then hoping for a dose of good fortune to actually spot them. And even when you spotted them, well, it wasn't the case that you could just drive off a single cow. No, you had to round them all up first – each one. Then, and only then, could you drive them off. If you didn't follow this procedure, you'd end up driving off one cow only to see another take its place behind you. Drive that one off, and the one you'd first taken care of would be back in the field busily munching on the sunflowers and leaving crescent moons in its wake. What's worse was that if you kept trying to drive off cows by themselves, all you ended up doing was aiding their digestion, which meant they ate even more.

No, the only thing to do was round them all up at the same time, drive one cow to another, then two cows to a third and so forth... What a bloody hassle. That year... I had no idea how many sunflowers remained untouched... probably not many. And there was no one to help, well, no one except Chouchou I suppose... It's just that... his assistance wasn't... well, it did more harm than good... I mean, there'd be no sign of Chouchou when I started, nor any sign of him after I'd put in a good many hours... He'd only appear after I had worked my arse off to get the cows all together... and then... he'd suddenly come racing up from out of nowhere, howling and barking without a care, driving straight into the herd to start nipping at their hooves... And what would happen? The cows would disperse, and I'd be back at square one again.

But what could I do? Nothing, really, other than curse Chouchou and once more start rounding up the cows.

Thinking about it some more, except for when I was in school and had to run the eight hundred metres, I'd never experienced anything as intense as the work in the fields. I hurt all over, truth be told. My chest was tight, and it was painful drawing in breaths, my throat was raw, tonsils enflamed... I swear my lungs had been worked over like bellows that were far too close to bursting.

To make matters worse, there was no time to rest, not even for a minute. Those bloody cows were too smart for it. If they discovered you were even a little bit tired, they'd be very quick to take liberties. If you ran, they would too... If you stopped, they'd follow suit. And then they'd continue munching on the sunflowers... *chomp, chomp, chomp...* without end... but always with their eyes directed towards me, waiting for any sign I might move, judging whether or not they were sufficiently far from me to flee should the need arise.

Afterwards, I could laugh at the whole experience. But when I was out there trying to round them up, it was hatred I felt. I'd kill them, eat their flesh and then sleep on their hides if I could... We were implacable enemies, bitterly opposed with neither side willing to give quarter. Uncle despised them even more... and he was even less inclined to show any mercy whatsoever. I threw stones, or chased after them with a long stick... Uncle, however, was more severe... he threw kitchen knives at them. When I saw him enraged like this, I couldn't do anything but follow after him... a cleaver in hand... then *whoooooshhh...* it'd fly through the air in the direction of one of the cows... And if he didn't strike bovine flesh on that first throw... he'd race forward to grab the knife once more and launch it again. I couldn't help but tremble a little at his ferocity...

On the one hand, I was secretly worried about my uncle's blood pressure and the growing chance of him suffering a stroke or cerebral haemorrhage... On the other hand, I prayed for the cows... it was the most I could do... for helping them was out of the question... Run a little faster... please run... Amitabha... please...

I suppose I had to thank my blessings, for I never did see Uncle once hit the mark.

My days were filled with trying to round up cattle, and so were my dreams. What's worse, in those dreams, my uncle's blades struck flesh... They'd run, and blood would flow freely... Out of all of the nightmares I've had, this was in the top three for sure.

It really was quite a challenge to round up the cattle, but it was even more difficult driving them. I mean, you could get them started well enough, get them moving forward, but if you turned, even for a minute, all forward advance would be lost, and you'd have to start all over again... No, the only option was to drive them relentlessly... *drive, drive, drive*... Crack the whip as it were... and keep at it until you reached the village... then turn around and head back?

Nah... it was all useless, for by the time you got back, those bloody cows would be there, too... If I quickened my pace, so would they. It's not like their legs could be tied, or the roads could be blocked... although that would be nice... I guess, in a manner of speaking, it was an all-day job... It's just too bad it wasn't someone else's job...

Finally, I came to a solution of sorts and decided to drive the cattle across the Ulungur and onto the northern shore. Once I got them to the riverbank, I threw stones again to urge the animals into the running water. Slowly but surely they edged in... one... then two... three... and soon the rest of the herd... I watched them as they shifted and bumped into each other... as they navigated the current... then reached the other side and finally crawled back up onto land... That's when I stopped throwing rocks at them.

I guess you could say all our problems were resolved – if the cows tried to cross back over, it was unlikely they would climb back up to where they had first entered the river. And as for a bridge crossing, that was dozens of kilometres up the river, quite far away from our land. And even if they did manage to get across once more, they'd have to traverse so many kilometres which would take so much time that ultimately their owner would appear and take charge of them.

Although Mum didn't participate much in our defensive war against the cattle, she was in fact quite good at it – that is, with relative ease, she could round the beasts up and drive them to a nearby pastureland left unused by one of our neighbours. Once they were there, Mum would bolt the fence, sealing them inside and away from our fields. She didn't care whose pastureland it was, and it didn't matter... she just had to get the cows off our land.

45

POWER

The cows seemed to love munching on the heads of the sunflowers. I suppose, to them, they were delicious. Better than grass at least. And certainly better than manufactured feed. Perhaps it was the seeds on the sunflowers the cows most enjoyed. I mean, even humans loved to eat those, especially people in the north of China. After all, whose house didn't have at least one or two members with so-called 'seed teeth'? You know, the small indentation worked into a tooth – usually the front incisor – due to cracking sunflower seeds. The winter slack season was so, so long in the north; if you didn't crack seeds, just what would you do?

But... what didn't make sense was that even I had these so-called 'seed teeth', and I hated sunflower seeds!

It's true, I didn't like putting them between my teeth. I didn't like their taste... I thought the flavour was much too strange... but... and this was a big but... although I couldn't stand them, once I cracked one... well, I couldn't stop. I would have to crack more and more, storing the shelled seeds in my left cheek like some chipmunk or other while I spat out the shells from my right cheek...

I really didn't like them, and in truth, my experience with cracking sunflower seeds was minimal... honest! But no one believed me, no matter what explanation I gave. Everybody could see my 'seed teeth' after all. Fine. Whatever. Even if I didn't enjoy eating the seeds, I had the teeth for it... It was just best not to mention anything about them, or cracking seeds.

Even Saihu loved sunflower seeds!

Although we'd had to replant several times in the spring, there were still some leftover seeds, and Mum simply threw them under the bed. This is where Saihu would find them, and in no time he would squirt in underneath the bed, and all we would hear would be a soft rustling noise as she devoured the flavourful, savoury dessert.

But Saihu couldn't crack the seeds herself, so she'd consume the shell and all. When Mum realised this, she couldn't just let the poor creature continue eating the whole thing, so when she had some free time, she would shell the seeds on her behalf. Of course, it was tiresome work, meaning Mum cursed the whole time. "Fuck... what am I doing this for? I work all friggin' day, and here I am back at home waiting on a bloody dog!"

After she cracked the shells, she'd leave the seeds in her hand for Saihu to gobble up. Unsurprisingly, Saihu's tail would wag furiously at the extra convenience in eating the sunflower seeds. This, in turn, would bring a great smile to Mum's face. If you were to look at things from a certain angle, I suppose it would appear as though we were short on actual dog food. But from another perspective, it emphasised how good sunflower seeds really were.

As for the rabbits and chickens, well, there's really nothing to say about them. After we harvested the seeds from the sunflower heads, threw out the remainders and packed up the produce, Mum gave whatever was left over to the rabbits and chickens. For them, it was a heavenly feast.

When it came time to sell the seeds, we'd always put a little to one side, and this is what we would bring to the sunflower oil pressing plant. Some of the oil we'd sell at Mum's store, the rest was for us to use... about a year's worth, which wasn't bad. The dregs that remained after pressing the crop to make the oil was also useful stuff; even though the best of it had already been ground out, the chickens and rabbits would still go mad for it like a bandit goes mad for gold.

It was almost hard to believe that such barren, infertile soil could bear such flavourful food. Thinking of it like this, I had to admire the power of the earth to produce what it did. And I guess the power of fertilisers, too. But still, fertilisers only aided the plants that the earth already deemed worthy to grow. Now it is true humans have researched means by which to grow plants without soil – so-called hydroponic techniques – but they could do nothing to change the rules pertaining to how things grew on the land. These rules were determined by the earth... That was its form of power for sure.

Mum didn't like using fertilisers. But like other farmers, there was really no way to avoid using them. When she was young, she'd studied books on the agricultural industry, on methods and techniques, and there was this one teacher who told her and her classmates that using fertilisers was akin to trying to seek instant gratification... that it was a short-sighted approach. Although it did increase yields, the teacher told them, continued use would destroy the soil after thirty years or so and then there would be no going back. She'd often recite that refrain: "It's already been thirty years, hasn't it?" I couldn't tell if it was worry in her voice, or doubt. In truth, I didn't know what it meant for the earth to be destroyed – that was a concept that I couldn't get my head around. But I have seen dead land.

I mean, really dead – the surface was hard and blanched white. The footpaths between the fields remained, tight together, orderly, neat and completely empty. If you angled your head, the fields spread out beyond the horizon like a great white washboard, the undulating bulges marking the footpaths, the dips being the empty farmland. Well, not completely empty – they were filled with the dead and decaying corpses of so many sunflower seeds from so many years before. The unrelenting sun had bleached them as well. I figured this was on account of the overuse of fertilisers, the unreliable irrigation, the alkalisation of the soil, the overextension of... lost and abandoned land.

The Gobi was dry and hard, too, but it was a normal part of the ecosystem, and its hardness was to be expected. It was desolate, but it did support life – a thin, rarefied layer, but life nonetheless. And yes, these bits of vegetation had sort of held on against all the odds. They were dark and rough, but they were alive. The fields I had seen were an unnatural desolation. The soil was crusted and cracked, almost as though it had been washed clean and sterilised. Not a single blade of grass grew. There was nothing living at all on that land. Like old, dead skin laid out over the body of the earth... that's what it was like. The only consolation was the wind knew no boundaries, so when it picked up, it would loosen and lift up the old, dried crusty earth... a great sandstorm that would conceal the devastation underneath. Day after day, the remaining droplets of water would disappear, leaving nothing but sand... hard, densely packed earth – like a mother holding on tightly to her dead child, refusing to let go but knowing there's nothing to be done.

Thinking of these things, my mind suddenly turned to the fate of the river. I'd heard of a river that ran through Altay. It flowed from the north and worked its way south. At its lower reaches, it emptied into a lake. But because the surrounding environment was terribly polluted, the lake had gradually become more of a swamp. I suppose you could say that it too had become trapped in a creeping form of desolation, or perhaps it was its last chance to fight. Its deterioration into a swamp could be a new lease on life, a transformation into a lung for the earth, a hardworking filter trying to decompose man's filth, man's hurt on the environment, its last gasp at trying to save a nearly hopeless cause.

"This isn't even our land," Mum cried, "and yet my heart breaks to see it like this! How could they have let it become like this!"

She was right, of course. But still I wondered... was it only farmers who could love and cherish the land? Was it only genuine people of the soil – those of us who relied upon the land for life itself, generation after generation – who could appreciate its importance? Real farmers would use a plot of land for a few years then leave it be for several more years and let it heal itself before using it again. Or in cases where particularly vigorous plants had been grown, those that demanded a lot of the land like sunflowers, they would be rotated off the plots and replaced by crops that were much gentler – plants that demanded less, such as alfalfa. Crop rotation was essential, just as it was necessary for shepherds to vary their routes so that the same piece of land was not overused. After all, that's why the herds were always on the move – to give time for the land to rest and recuperate.

I worried a great deal about the barren, northern landscape. Although the fields that had been used to grow crops all looked very much the same – neat, tidy, lush – when I looked at wild fields again, I knew that the land in the south was green and abundant, the vegetation dense all the year through. The opposite was the case in the north – the plant cover was frail and weak, unvaried and easily prone to destruction. But while the soil was considered weak and vulnerable in the north, according to the people who populated these regions, it was enough to make a living on...

If not for those of us who came up here to plunder it...

No one owned the land up here. Those of us who used it to grow crops were guests. We rented it for a year, maybe two, maybe three. That's why it was in the state it was... far too many of us had neglected to follow the natural order of things. We were here for a relatively short period of time, and so many of us thought we had to get the most out of the land as possible, regardless of the long-term consequences... That's why the soil was extorted for everything it had. That's why so much of it had been killed... murdered. It was bound to be transformed into desert or crusted, dead land. All that was left was a thin layer of plastic mulch, the remains of far too many pesticide containers and other bits of man-made destruction.

That's when the rental period ended.

The land we'd rented had already been used for three years. This meant it should have been left fallow in order to give it time to recover, for at least two years, especially since the previous tenants had grown hungry sunflowers that demanded so much of the soil. After all, if the earth had been subject to such an all-consuming crop, not only would the damage be extensive, but the possibility of productive yields in the future would also be diminished. What's more, at that time our only option was to buy the seeds the land had already produced. In many ways, this was akin to negotiating a marriage between relatives, that is, if the same seeds were planted back into the same soil whence they came, there'd be an obvious and unavoidable decline in quality. Further complicating things was the legacy of the previous winter's weather. The rare and unusual warmth experienced then meant drought conditions were inevitable.

The news of this had already spread in all directions.

Mum persevered, however; she was going to use all of her energy to plant again this year, and if she couldn't depend on the river, then she'd bet on the rain. Why, you might ask? Well, it had to do with what she'd heard from an old local Kazakh man who'd told her that if, during the Nowruz Festival to welcome in the New Year, usually sometime in March, there was a great deal of rain, then that would bode well for a wet year with a lot of rainfall.

"An old man told me this, you know," Mum explained. "You gotta trust their words after all." And so she staked everything on the man's words, sold our house and bet the farm, quite literally, on a productive growing season.

And do you know what? It rained a lot that year – practically every day.

But at the same time as the rain fell hard, the wind also accompanied it... Before a few raindrops could land on the parched earth, dark clouds formed in the sky and a gale blew through. The rain could do nothing but submit to the more powerful force of nature. Despite the heavy losses, and even the need to abandon the land, Mum, at that moment, was very gratified to finally see the river gush forth like a hail of bullets. By the time things reached this stage, whatever compensation there might be coming couldn't be anything but a cheat.

Each time I had to drive the cattle around and around the sunflower fields, all in the effort to defend our last victory, the ripening of the flowers, I would inevitably be huffing and puffing, gasping for breath so hard that I feared my lungs were about to explode, and my mind would wander to this: we've completely overdrawn on the payment the earth has given us, and it is now up to us to use our own power to supplement it.

The sunflowers were harvested. The one-hundred-plus mu of fields produced twenty-plus tonnes of sunflower seeds, all loaded to the brim into four-hundred-plus sacks piled together on the ground. Looking at them, we couldn't help but feel a sense of satisfaction, and even a bit of happiness, too. That, unfortunately, didn't last, for even though everything was ready to be moved onto the trucks that would carry the seeds to market, there were no hired hands around to help us. Of course, this caused no small amount of worry for both Mum and my uncle, for time was already short – we'd been delayed after all, and we really couldn't wait any longer. Finally, there was little else we could do to begin to move the sacks ourselves. I say move, not load, because the trucks that were to carry the seeds couldn't drive all the way to where they were piled together, which meant they had to carry all of them about thirty or so metres to where the vehicles were parked.

Four hundred bags... After two hundred were moved, Mum and my uncle returned. More than thirty metres – factoring in the weight of each bag and the distance, each person walked six to seven kilometres. I say we had to carry it, but really it was only Mum and Uncle, which meant together these two old fogeys moved over two hundred tonnes of sunflower seeds thirty-plus metres. To put it another way, they each carried fifty-kilo sacks six to seven kilometres. I guess the only benefit of this was that they saved another two hundred yuan that would've had to have been spent on workers' wages.

But my uncle's high blood pressure...

My mum's low blood pressure...

In an instant, the bright, dazzling wealth represented by the sunflower seeds had transformed into a dense, dark, heavy mass. It had not only pressed its weight down upon the earth but was now also crushing a poor husband and wife.

46

A BEAUTIFUL SCENE

I can't recall how many times I walked along lonely, deserted fields, my mind caught up with thoughts about the land beneath my feet and its fate. The more I would walk, the more the wind would pick up. Gradually, I would arrive at the highest point of the Ulungur River. There, facing the wind, I could hear it violently whistle all about me, filling the sky with its high-pitched shriek. Standing abreast this great river, swallowed whole by the booming wind, all other sounds were drowned out. But... if I shifted just a little, my perspective changed, my ears heard something different, and the roar of the wind suddenly receded. Another moment passed, and then a great *pop* resounded immediately below my feet. I was enveloped within a vacuum, peaceful and calm. Only my hair and the edge of my skirt blew in the wind, proving that it still swirled around me. It was just that my ears were somehow behind a protective screen, spared the incessant howl of the wind.

Standing on the highest point, perched, as it were, on the dividing line between the clamour of the wind outside and the quiet enfolding my ears, I felt as though I were some object thrusting myself against both the noise and the silence. In front of my eyes, however, spread the desolate sunflower fields, their barren stalks arranged in an orderly fashion alongside the riverbank, disappearing over the horizon. The trees that ran adjacent to the fields and the desolation that reached out beyond them stood as a verdant dividing line; a leafy, green stretch of life holding out against the voraciousness of the Gobi, coming up hard against it in an act of lush defiance.

The constant work demanded of the harvesting season was finally drawing to a close. I no longer needed to worry about the cows, nor did I need to drive them anywhere. There was more and more time to relax and shoot the breeze. My days all began at the yurt, and then I would find myself walking far and wide in nearly all directions. I would do this until the sky hung low on the western horizon and the temperature began to drop. Then I would finally make my way slowly back to my starting point.

Sometime after, I discovered a most beautiful little spot. From then on, besides this small oasis, I went nowhere else. This spot was located on the eastern side of the fields, near a small, shallow brook that ran with crystal clear water. (The same place I'd once tried to bathe in.) I'd only just realised the place possessed an unusual topography – a ledge the shallow brook fell over creating a smallish but oh-so-beautiful waterfall. The stream must've cast itself over the precipice for an age because directly below it the ground had been carved out forming a small pool of water.

The pool was not large – about the size of a double bed, nothing more – but it was incredibly deep and clear all the way to the bottom. Pure white sand surrounded the water, and at its edge grew a grove of reeds. A small, straight path cut towards the pool; it could've only been cut by the cows.

Each time I walked here, I did so alone, winding and wending my way along my own small path. I would then push my way through the reeds like I was ripping wrapping paper off a present, my heart filled with genuine excitement. In this great monotonous expanse, this little pool could be nothing else but an accident. The surprise and joy the scene gave rise to in my heart were no less than that experienced by tourists visiting the nation's five-star attractions.

What's more, this spot was a secret known only to me, which served to make it even more beautiful.

When the wind picked up and buffeted my little oasis with its aggressive power, the reeds would be thrown about, and I thought I could hear the holler of some unseen person; I feared terribly that my secret spot would be forcefully exposed. I'd feel an almost overwhelming need to voice tearful complaints... to justify... to apologise... but when I tried to open my mouth, the only words that ushered forth were those in awe of the sanctuary I'd found. I was like a sinless man using all my powers to praise the beauty of the scene. Again and again, my praise reached into the sublime, azure sky above, and it thrust into the formidable and endless power of the wind; praise for this hidden gem of a location I'd found amongst the barren landscape. It was as though the earth had offered up this place in response to the admiration I had shown it.

But my heart understood this world didn't need my admiration. In truth, it didn't need me... it never did. It was *me* who needed the world.

The wind gradually eased, and the world grew quiet. My heart, too, felt the excitement leave it.

My uncle also visited the secret pool. Afterwards, he described it in detail to us: "A gorgeous place, beautiful, unbelievably so! We ought to get a metal fence to encircle the area, and then, later on, construct a building or two, a few tables... Ah... it could be a great draw for tourism."

He used more or less the same words to describe each and every beautiful place he saw. Mum's response to beautiful scenery was much more muted. She would simply click her tongue and remark that such and such a view or place was pretty, yes, quite pretty.

At times, I felt as though only the three of us knew of the secret lagoon. Then, when I was out walking in the wilderness, I couldn't help but feel that whosoever was out here would somehow find the same place. Why else would they seemingly have that knowing smile?

I went there every day and concealed myself within its beauty. I guess you could say I was rather attached to it. There were even times when I dreamed of staying there forever... But dreams are only ever that – dreams... hopes never realised, fragile by their very nature.

With the harvest finished, I was destined to leave here forever. I would never see my precious refuge again. As this realisation dawned on me, a great feeling of hate welled up inside me. I despised my itinerant life, my ability to make my home wherever my head lay. I hated those strange beds, the unfamiliar rooms, the forever foreign lands... I hated it all...

47

GOING FOR A WALK

One day when Mum came back from the fields, she talked repeatedly, and in the highest, most praiseworthy terms possible, about a... a godlike cat – her words – that she'd come across earlier in the day.

"Let me tell you..." Mum began. "The creature was ever so adept at following people. Wherever someone went, the cat would be close behind... I saw it several times... and each time it was the same..."

"What's so strange about that?" I asked.

"Have you ever seen a cat spend the entire day following its owner around?"

I thought this over for a spell and had to admit that I hadn't. Every cat I'd ever seen had always been a solitary creature, a predator prowling along by itself. It was probably more common to see a person chasing after a cat, not the other way around. Oh no, cats walked on their own, they had no stomach to play the lackey for man. The cats I'd seen, well, they'd only curl up around your legs when they wanted something, or if they were in some kind of danger, a threat to their life, or something like that... say when the temperature dropped well past freezing, or when they'd been wounded somehow, or they were hungry, especially for a treat, or when they needed a suitable, safe environment to bear a litter of kittens. That was when they showed up, when they needed a human's help.

But the cat Mum spoke about was nothing like this. It behaved in an entirely different way. I saw it once, too, sometime after... It really was a peculiar sight.

The family in question was responsible for the neighbouring plot of land. And there were a lot of them. We'd see them file out in the morning to begin work, and then file back in when the sun set. Each time, they'd pass by the irrigation trenches to the west, and each time the cat would follow them to work as though it were tending to the fields as well; it even carried itself in the same manner as the field hands did... it was really quite something. I mean, it always held its head high, striding along confidently as though it had worked as hard as everyone else.

"Whaddya think..." Mum questioned me, "if I were to ask them to give me the cat, do you think they would?"

"I heard they want more, which is odd considering the size of their family... How could you go about asking them... I mean, what would you say?"

She thought this over for a few minutes before replying: "Then I'll ask to borrow it... I'll tell them we've got mice and that we need a cat for a few days. Then, once it's here, I'll feed it like it's never been fed before. It'll want to stay after that... probably... And then when it's time to return the animal... well... we'll just refuse." She paused for a moment as though something had just occurred to her. "Besides," she added, "they're from away... Their sunflower fields are suffering much more from the lack of water than ours, too... Who's to say they won't just give up and leave... And if that happens, who'll even remember that they've lent us their cat."

"Do you really think the... the cat is worth the trouble?"

"It's special... for sure... It follows them out into the fields."

The following day, she paid them a visit and made her dubious request, even if she stammered all the while she spoke. Surprisingly, at least to me, was that they believed Mum's story and gave her the cat. At first, Mum was equally surprised and happy... She couldn't believe they'd part with it, and said as much to them. Their response startled Mum even more.

"It's not even our bloody cat... and it keeps following us everywhere... no matter how hard we've tried to get rid of it... Damned nuisance."

Mum didn't say anything further, nor did she ask any more questions. She just held on tight to the animal and left as quickly as she could. Once back home, she couldn't resist but shower the creature with affection and kisses. "You're home now, sweetie. From this day onwards, we're your family!"

I suppose you could say the cat had the habit of falling in love with people. It was a... a people cat, instead of the usual loner feline skulking off to do who knows what. It not only trailed after us but was also incredibly obedient and submissive, to both me and Mum. In a way, it was more like a stuffed animal, or a dead one, as we could push it as much as we wanted, or cuddle and scratch the back of its head to our hearts' content. It wasn't picky about food, and it could catch mice, too. It was a very... economical cat... I guess that's one way of putting it. At least, that was what we thought that first day. On the following one, we saw some of its true colours. Or rather, Chouchou did, for the cat, much smaller than him I should note, attacked him so viciously that we didn't see the poor dog for a good two days... He was simply too afraid to return...

Let me tell you, if I hadn't seen it with my own eyes, I never would've believed it! After all, Chouchou was huge compared to it, and seemingly much fiercer to boot! I mean, he was as big as a calf, if not bigger, and would chase after gazelles out in the fields as though it was a game. He was a shoe thief, too, prone to giving us all a merry chase should we even try to apprehend him to get him to give up his loot.

But when he was face to face with that cat, well, he was more like a terrified house rat than anything else.

Their first confrontation lasted but a second. The cat hissed but once and then proceeded to attack, violently jumping at poor Chouchou, its claws sharp, its teeth sharper. Chouchou was completely stunned. He'd never before encountered anything like this small ball of feline ferocity. After all, weren't there supposed to be negotiations first, then a declaration of war? The cat followed neither procedure – it simply attacked without even bothering to let Chouchou declare his position. Poor Chouchou... he didn't have even a second to react before the cat was on top of him, biting at his throat.

The cat's assault was perfect, vicious and precise. Once it had sunk its teeth into Chouchou's flesh, it wouldn't let go. Its claws, too, dug into him like a vice. Chouchou responded with a yelp that betrayed the pain and fear he felt. He then started twisting and turning, bouncing and jumping, all in the effort to get the beast off of him. Finally, he succeeded, and the cat twirled in the air before landing on its feet on the ground. A second later and it launched its second assault; its teeth once more sunk into flesh. It showed no hesitation in its attack; it gave no quarter. It was relentless, even howling like some big jungle cat to instil more fear and awe in its enemy.

This was no simple country cat; it was more a tiger than anything else!

Mum and I just watched the scene unfold, wholly mesmerised by what we were witnessing, forgetting, too, to even try and rescue poor Chouchou.

Poor Chouchou indeed... he had lost not only the initiative but also his courage. All he could do was whine and wail, overwhelmed by the cat's ferociousness, its intensity. Needless to say, our impression of Chouchou was severely dampened; he'd lost face... that much was certain. That was when we realised we had to do something; we had to save him; we had to pull the cat off of him. He didn't thank us – no, he just let his tail fall between his legs and fled.

The cat won its first battle decisively. On the third day, it struck again while the iron was still hot and bit a cow as it trod alongside the yurt. A cow... I'm serious... An animal two hundredfold larger... at least... It didn't vary its tactics, either. They were enemies – there was no doubt that's how the cat felt. Its eyes betrayed the feeling acutely, and attack was its only option. I've seen other cats fight before; their backs arch, their fur rises, and they let out a hiss to warn their opponent to make no further moves. Their eyes are like daggers trying to will their enemy into submission. Next, they bare their teeth, shift their feet into an appropriate attack posture, and then, if all of this fails to dissuade their adversary, they fight. But this cat employed none of these tactics. It ignored any and all rules of combat. The Geneva Conventions meant nothing to it.

If its brutality transformed a dog into a house rat, its assault on the cow transformed it into a dog. It was startled, frightened and hurt. Its head tilted towards the sky, and it neighed in pain. A moment later it began bucking, trying as hard as it could to throw the cat off its back. Once it succeeded, it, like Chouchou, fled, disappearing quickly like a wisp of smoke that leaves no trace. All I could think was that I wished I'd had that cat before, driving those blasted cattle away from the fields would've been a helluva lot easier for sure!

After these two battles, the cat had established its position at the top of the pecking order. When Mum and I thought to scratch the back of the cat's head, or to nestle it in any way, we couldn't help but hesitate. Would we... could we be next? Later, we began to worry whether or not the cat would exert its suzerainty over Saihu and the chickens. As it happened, however, the cat didn't perceive them as potential threats, and so it paid them no heed; they were small fry after all.

That's right... I began this chapter talking about going for a walk.

The final bit of work in the sunflower fields had ended, and now all we had to do was wait for the day they were to be sold. Since there was nothing else to do, each evening after dinner, the whole family would go out for a walk. And I do mean everyone – the cat, Saihu, even the braver rabbits would accompany us. Chouchou, too, who always loved joining in the fun, wouldn't miss out either, although his fear of the cat kept him some distance behind. There were also some chickens who tagged along, those that hadn't already settled down in their coop for the night. At first, there'd be a few, but they'd gradually turn and head back. Chickens, after all, had a hard time seeing in the dark, and since the sun had set by the time we started on our stroll, most of them had difficulty seeing very far in front of them. The braver ones remained for as long as they could, but eventually they'd only be able to cluck and stumble around, walking a few steps at best. That was when Mum would turn and pick up the few that still remained, carrying them in her arms as we continued our evening stroll.

"What about the ducks, hmm, should we take them with us too? Whaddya think, would they even come with us?" She wouldn't wait for me to reply. I guess it wasn't really a question, at least not one she wanted answered. No, she'd just go on talking to herself, commenting on the supposed wealth we had, and how good every-one… everything behaved.

What a sight we must've been. A great group of people, and animals, there, walking through the night, under the glow of a full moon, the wind blowing and Mum as happy as she could be. I imagine we looked much like a circus, with Mum as the ringmaster, leading her charges on the way to the city, advertising our own 'greatest show on earth'. I suppose she also might've looked like a tour guide, and we her enraptured tourists… It's too bad she didn't have a loudspeaker with her – she'd fit the part for sure… *All right everyone, come along, hold on tight to your cameras and be sure to snap pictures!*

I have to admit, I remember those walks very fondly indeed. They were so peaceful, so relaxed. My heart was so full of happi-ness then. I swear my feet had wings and I could fly… On those walks, I don't know, but it seemed as though all my hopes and dreams could come true; those walks were certainly more enjoy-able than anything.

"Hey…" Mum broke the silence we were walking in. "I heard they sell breast enhancement cream in the city… Is that right?"

"Breast enhancement?"

"Yeah, you know the stuff – you rub it into your breasts, and they're supposed to get bigger."

I glanced at her chest. "And *why* do you want that?"

She seemed pleased with herself. "Let me tell you, I've thought of something. It's the best way, really. We'll take that cream and rub it into our dogs' ears – that'll make them grow, right? And then, well, they'll be perkier than ever before!"

I looked at them... It was true... their ears drooped quite a bit. They looked rather listless.

"You can't even take on a cat – it's no wonder your ears hang so low..."

What could I say, Mum was just being Mum. She had to have things to worry about, things to fuss over. The dogs' ears were just one such thing. I mean, she felt she had to meddle in everything – in how the cock treated the hens, how the dogs' ears sagged... There was even an incident with the cat... It got into a fight with some feral feline, and Mum was the one to grab a stick and help out, despite the offensive prowess we'd seen before in the cat... Every day, she moaned about how difficult it was taking care of such a crowd, how it pained her... But I suppose... that's what mums do... It was only during our walks that she felt totally at ease... It was like, in the still of night, she'd led us through the great expanse of wilderness to a quiet respite alongside the river... Or maybe we were a band of refugees fleeing some disaster or other, and she'd finally guided us to a place of rest, if only temporarily...

I had a dream, and in it we were still walking under the full moon... Everyone was there... Everything... Even the ducks. The sunflower seeds we'd grown had all been packed into hemp sacks... They were filled to the brim... then loaded onto trucks before departing and slowly disappearing over the horizon... Suddenly... my mind was drawn to memories of Granny, and I looked around, half expecting to find her... After I woke up.

48

THE HUMAN WORLD

On occasion, once we were back in the city, we'd bump into former acquaintances, former compatriots who used to work out in the sunflower fields. They always seemed to be so excited, so worked up about something or other. If we were to talk about feelings of friendship, well, it would be hard to say how deep such feelings went, or even if they were there at all. But there was a bond... of some sort, here, in the mass of people flowing through the city, in this sea of humanity. When you bumped into someone who shared the same experiences as you had, there was a special connection at least... a cordiality built on... on a shared knowledge of loneliness, I suppose.

Except for the time I ran into Bahiti.

I'd just left the main market square and turned the corner when I came upon a man urinating against the wall. His back faced the street, and a rubbish bin partially blocked my view. There was a slight rustling sound. I was embarrassed and thought to quickly spin around and leave without him noticing me, but just as I was about to do so, he turned his head, and our eyes met. I was going to pretend I hadn't seen him, but I was too late. I recognised who it was, and he recognised me. Before another moment passed, a great smile spread wide across his face... What could I do but smile brightly in return... He then smiled even more, and I could see his sincerity – he was happy to see me. He finished his business, pulled his trousers back up and began walking towards me, fastening his belt as he did so.

And then... he extended his hand for me to shake!

We exchanged conventional pleasantries, talked about this and that, all while I tried my utmost to pretend I hadn't seen his outstretched hand.

In all honesty, I didn't begrudge the meaning behind Bahiti's gesture. Nor was he offended by my failure to shake his hand. I have to add, too, that he felt no sense of embarrassment about how I had bumped into him. I suppose it was really only me being small-minded. Fine... I guess I was to blame... after all, I'd been the one wandering about, looking this way and that.

Bahiti's family lived in the village closest to the reservoir. He must've had some work arrangement in place for he was always going back and forth between the town and the hydro plant. And each time he completed whatever task he had to do, on his return he would go out of his way to stroll through the forest and drop in on us. He also owed my uncle fifty yuan, a debt he'd had for about twenty years. It was kind of funny in a way, for each time he visited, my uncle would first ask how things were, how he was doing – you know, small talk – and then he'd ask about the fifty yuan. Bahiti's response was always sincere. He didn't have it. Nothing else would be said about it. They'd just start talking about this and that. Gossiping, really.

In this world, it was far more common for a debtor to avoid his creditor, but for Bahiti and my uncle, it wasn't like that at all. Neither treated the other with anything but respect. Two equals, that's what they were, and a debt between them wouldn't change that.

Borrowing money is borrowing money, not paying it back is not paying it back, and there's really not much more to say. Being open about the situation means there's no need for one to be sorry to the other. Of course, the failure to repay the debt did make my uncle angry, but at the same time he had to admit that Bahiti was an honest, trustworthy old man.

Each time this honest old man visited our yurt, we'd exchange the usual greetings, share some tea, and then he would respectfully take his leave. His show of respect wasn't because he owed Uncle money, but rather because this was how he had been brought up. And his visits weren't because there was something wrong, or he was in need of something. No, he was simply passing by, and the only polite thing to do was to drop in and say hello. And not because he owed money – he was just being courteous and respectful, as was his way.

Down south, the shepherds and their herds had completed their crossing of the river, which meant more and more people started to filter back into the town. The influx of people meant Mum's store business picked up, which also resulted in her returning home later and later each day. Before, when we were busy with the sunflower fields, out in the wilderness, we'd rarely see anyone outside of our immediate family. I mean, besides the occasional hydro plant worker or Bahiti, or a passing shepherd or two, we were pretty much on our own. If it happened to be a shepherd, we'd greet each other cordially enough, and then I would criticise them for not looking after their cattle better than they were; the damn beasts, I would tell them, were constantly trampling all over our sunflowers. Their response to my accusations was nothing if not expected.

"Weren't my cows!"

Unfortunately, I was quite helpless in proving otherwise as of course there'd be no damn cow in the area. Thereafter, they'd always pop round for tea if they happened to come by, and I would always tell them I was watching them closely.

Slowly but surely, the herds of sheep crossed the river as well. Fortunately for us, we had already completed the harvest, and the seeds had all been packed into their hemp sacks. Occasionally, the herdsmen would drive their sheep into the harvested field and allow them to munch on the remaining bits of bare stems and the seeds that had been crushed and left lying on the ground. The herdsmen wouldn't stay to watch them at times like these. No, they'd instead come and knock on our door, expecting to be invited in for tea.

It was times like these that our yurt was much like every other home out here in the wilderness – lively and filled with guests. By this time, I fully understood that coming in for tea wasn't just to quench their thirst; it was also a means by which they could establish relationships with the other inhabitants living on the plains. That said, during these visits I never heard them say anything much more than their parents' names and where they came from. There was, I suppose, little by way of shared topics to talk about beyond the mundane. Still, they always seemed to be in fine moods, despite the shortness of the conversations, and once they had introduced themselves and finished their tea, they stood respectfully and said their goodbyes. And that was it.

We also had a number of women pay us visits during this time. But to this day, I don't know why they came, nor for what purpose.

There was nothing beyond the hydro plant. There was the odd time when sheep were left to graze out beyond the plant, or when herdsmen were out searching for their cattle, but there was no proper road to traverse. It was, as they say, a dead end. But these women... they'd appear as though out of nowhere, dressed for a night out on the town, with the makeup to match. They certainly didn't look like herders out in search of their cows, nor shepherds in charge of sheep. That much was plain to see. And if we were to say they had come out to the station to carry out some special or important task and had decided to drop in on Mum as well, to be frank, they just didn't look the part. No, the only possibility was that they'd come out here specifically to visit Mum. They'd come to gossip.

We hadn't been in the area for two months yet, but already our yurt was part of the landscape as though it had been here forever. And this seemed all so natural and inevitable. What's more, we'd all become part of the local community, such as it was, and every snippet of news or gossip – no matter how big or small, salacious or not – ended up on Mum's doorstep... She was always kept in the loop.

It's true that in general Mum's spoken Kazakh wasn't the best and she ended up stuttering and stammering more than anything else, but each time the local ladies came to share details of some such tale or other, her ability to use the language increased noticeably. As a result, it no longer mattered how difficult the means to express something was, Mum was no longer anxious or impatient when trying to find the words to say it best. In fact, the women would be more than accommodating. Sitting around in a circle, they'd switch back and forth between Kazakh and Mandarin, neither language taking precedence. Only the topic remained key – that was what was important, what couldn't be abandoned.

After the women left, Mum would give me the condensed version, and whole new worlds would be open to my eyes. At the same time, I would be flabbergasted. We'd been here for months, had lived alongside them, but in all that time, I hadn't learned as much about life out here than Mum had learned in those ten minutes of gossiping. I was even more gobsmacked when I realised that such scandalous and altogether shocking events could happen out here in the middle of friggin' nowhere, in a supposedly quiet and quaint little county town, isolated and far removed from everything, and with a small population to boot.

It wasn't just about us having a relatively smooth go at harvesting our sunflowers; the buying and selling season for the herdsmen, both sheep and cow, had also arrived. It wasn't just about us being able to relax since we'd finished in the fields; it was also a time for everyone else to enjoy the riches they'd earned the past season and to finally take it down a gear and enjoy some small comforts.

Our last visitor before we departed was the former farmer who'd tended the same sunflower fields before us. While we chatted, for some unknown reason the discussion wound its way to my age and to the fact that I wasn't married, which caused no small amount of shock to the man – so much so that he had to repeatedly ask me to reconfirm that I was indeed still single. Once he'd left, I had no idea what we had talked about.

That evening, after it had already grown quite dark, the man again showed up at our yurt. Evidently, he'd grabbed a torch and made his way through the night, all the way to tell me he'd act as a go-between in finding me a man... He wanted to introduce me to a man who lived in Turpan, in Toqsun County... His only condition was that the woman he'd marry had to move to live in Turpan. All right then, he wanted to act as a go-between... What could I do but begin to imagine the ins and outs of it – in faraway Toqsun Nahiyisi, there was a young man, a bachelor, who, for reasons unknown, or perhaps just because of the various bumps along the road, had gradually become an older young man, still a bachelor. Later, again for reasons that had not been made clear, he'd not been able to find a suitable bride... And yet, like so many other people, he firmly believed in fate, that the ideal person was out there and he was destined to meet them, no matter what...

So a net had been cast far and wide with him at the centre... a radius that now reached over eight hundred kilometres... all the way from Toqsun to the sunflower fields where I lived.

I was still a part of this human world, I suppose. Or at least, way out here on the edge of nowhere, societal ideas of marriage and its imagined necessity were still able to track me down. Akin to a honeybee being drawn to what it is for reasons it cannot fathom, or like a labourer who can do nothing but surrender to the unavoidable suffering of work, there are still times when flowers bloom, when feelings like love find form, and lust and desire need to be satisfied. That time had apparently come... marriage... and all that it meant...

If only I wasn't me, then things would be all right. If only I was like other girls who thirsted and longed for a man to sweep her off her feet... then perhaps I could try... the life of another person... eight hundred kilometres away...

But I often hallucinate... I feel as though I am slipping away, that my body and this sunflower field are gradually retreating into dreams and fiction... Our guests are increasingly unable to pull us back... Even the weightiness of the harvest, the cold, hard reality of a fated marriage... none of it could pull us back... My mind returned to the sunflower fields we'd abandoned in the south... They'd already been lost to dreams... More than once I'd urged Mum to find the time so that we could go and see them... Her hesitancy betrayed what was on her mind... She wondered if that plot of land still really existed or not.

AFTERWORD

1

Thinking back to those times, there are so many paths, so many roads that lead to different memories of those golden fields, but there are no paths that can take me through those remembrances. Writing these words, I have a countless number of ways to start, but I can't find a suitable ending. I'll put the cause of this inability on the words themselves. I feel they were just unwilling to come to a stop. What's more, the life they described, well, that hasn't come to an end either. At least not yet. I've tried to express my emotions as best I can, but I guess things have come to a somewhat abrupt stop. I suppose, if I think about it some more, the real reason for this predicament has to do with the most central, key aspect of that life... I've just been unwilling to touch on it myself. Or perhaps I'm just unable, and I lack the skill...

2

But do you know what? I've long wanted to write about all of this. Write about the land, about the myriad things that inhabit it, about the things that have disappeared and what still remains. And most of all, I've wanted to write about... us... people... and our relationship with this world – about our hopes and desires and passions, about our innocence and our greed. Before I picked up the pen, I already felt an urgency to write. Afterwards, with the pen in hand, I couldn't help but feel I'd been thrust into some sort of labyrinth. Time and again, I could see myself drawing close to my objective, and then, gradually but surely, it would move farther and farther away. As a result, these words here on the page are, in truth, a narrative full of so many detours.

3

This business probably arose about ten years ago. But I've only written about the first two years of our experience tending the land, planting sunflowers. In the third year of farming, the long-hoped-for bumper harvest at last arrived. It was also a year that changed everything. Uncle had gone to the market to sell the last batch of seeds, and then, while he was on his way home, he was struck down by a cerebral haemorrhage... a sudden stroke that left him paralysed. He hasn't recovered from it either. He can't take care of himself anymore. He can't even speak. Neither he nor Mum returned to the fields after that.

4

Sunflowers cast a beautiful image; they truly are a beautiful emblem. It's true, too, that they're often associated with ideas of passion and valour. When I was writing this book, I frequently found myself relying on this imagery. But... I think the sunflowers disagree on this point. Talking about the seeds, the fresh sprouts that push up through the ground, the stems that begin to branch out, the flowers that bloom, the new seeds that are produced, the barren stalks, the oil, the dregs that are left over after harvesting – they all disagree with this assessment.

Of course, their main objective is to blossom when the time is right, to dazzle their surroundings with their golden magnificence. But most of their lives are spent waiting, bearing patiently until the season calls for them to bloom. If they were people, they'd possess a great forbearance; we'd call them eminently pragmatic. If they were dogs, then we'd describe them as being incredibly earnest, intelligent and sensible.

Most people are just in it for the splendid beauty of the sunflowers. Our passion lies in grasping it as quickly as we can. No one's interested in how the flower got there.

My words skirted too much, avoided too much. I feel that's because these things were not worth mentioning. But in my heart, I know that is not the case. It understands. I avoided these things because of my own cowardice and vanity.

5

I still dream of being out in the fields, tending to the land. But it's only a dream – there's no way to make it a reality. I do long to have a small home with a courtyard close to the wilderness, though. Even just a small piece. Enough land to plant some peppers and tomatoes, a few rows of chives. Enough for me to have a cat, perhaps two or three chickens. Two rooms would be enough. A table, a chair, a bed, a pot, a bowl, that'd be enough. Such a place would be more complete than the wealthiest of wealthy kingdoms.

But the real... me... is not like this at all. I have too many clothes stuffed into my wardrobe, enough bowls and kitchen utensils to fill a sink. My life... my days... are preoccupied with silly trivial things, by anxieties and worries. I never feel ready... never feel sufficiently prepared to carry out whatever tasks I may need to. And then when I'm finished, I still only ever worry about my own personal gains and losses – not whether what I've done has been done correctly. I attribute all of this to my lack of that small piece of land, to my lack of a suitable fate. Nonetheless, no matter how I might try to chase after this, I'll never be well enough prepared to actually get it.

In Sichuan, when I was but a child, I used to run and play all over the place. I'd see the farmer tending the fields, doing the same work over and over again, day in and day out. Work like stirring a long plastic ladle through a container of diluted faecal matter... night soil... fertiliser... shit... and then spreading it over his crops, each plant getting an equal amount. There was so much greenery, row upon row; such a giant field, such loneliness, such weakness. And still he persevered, carried on the monotonous work, over and over again, day after day. I imagine his heart was as calm and tranquil as those many other ancients who had tended the land for thousands of years before him.

I'd never felt such tranquillity. I suppose I never will. I couldn't help but envy those farmers in the fields, those boys in the front seat who never needed to look behind them.

6

I suppose being a writer means the words I put down on the page are what I plant? Maybe. In a sense, I could say I'm immersed in words... trapped even... Each word... each sentence, once it reaches the page, is evidence of the painstaking efforts I've had to endure to create the stories I have. Each and every word is engraved on my mind, inscribed on my heart as though I have no other choice but to brood over them. I want... I need to write them down... figure out why they so occupied my mind, monopolised my memory. Writing is akin to thrusting a spade into the ground, and shifting the earth to see what's there underneath; it's an adventure of discovery, I suppose. Indeed, there have been many times when I'm writing when I just can't help but go "Oh!" as though I've hit upon something unexpected. I've found that in many cases writing challenges and destabilises those things I've firmly trusted in the past. There're things I've thought I've forgotten, but then when I write, these things come rushing back; they suddenly burst forth from my pen to inhabit the page. I depend on writing. I believe in it. On many occasions, I suppose I've felt my fair share of satisfaction with writing, with this fate that I've been given.

7

The last bit I need to talk about is the photos in the book. I must apologise because they do not do justice to the sunflower fields – most of the scenes are of that first year in the countryside, as well as of the life in Akehala two years after that. (I added these photos as a means to complement the image I've given of my life there, and Akehala is really the only other place intimately connected to it. Originally, we'd planned to live there for a long time, to settle there, and that's why we turned to farming.)

That first year I went out there, I took along with me a digital camera. I snapped a few pics of farmers sowing seeds. At the time, I didn't dare take too many photos... I only had two batteries... and in the summer I planned to head to the pasturelands... Needless to say, there was nowhere to charge the batteries, or get replacements, nothing but wild grasslands and pasture, I had to be as careful with the batteries as I could.

The next year, Mum brought a solar battery with her out into the wilderness, so I could finally recharge my camera – that is, if I had one. Luckily, I had my mobile and could take photos with it. Afterwards, as I mentioned in the book, I lost my phone. Not long after, I broke my flash drive, so I lost my backup, too.

Again, as I wrote in the book, I firmly believe those images are still there on that broken drive, patiently waiting... I hope for the day I can repair it. When I was out in the sunflower fields, my mobile was my means to confront the quiet loneliness of the scene in front of me... press down on the shutter. There's not much difference between the me of then and the me of now. My heart will forever harbour this deep, intense longing... That's why I've got no choice but to write about it and tell as many people as I can.

Let me express my gratitude, then, to all of you for listening to me.

Lastly, I'd like to thank all of those readers who read earlier versions of these words, for your enthusiasm and helpful comments. Thanks are due to my editor, too, for the encouragement and the patience when it took me longer than intended to finish. I suppose I should thank myself, too. Although I don't think I'm ever able to do my best, I'm grateful for my honesty and persistence in keeping at it, in writing these words here for others to enjoy.

- 26 September 2017

After Mum and Saihu have walked past, the barren wilderness and old dirt road is left empty.

The work on our 'hole' is nearly complete.

My granny standing in amongst our things scattered haphazardly about the empty land.

Our first evening out here in the wilderness. Granny was starving by this point, whereas Mum continued to work.

Our first morning.

Our sunflower fields. That's Saihu sniffing in the dirt. Some wild pigeons are doing the same nearby. Saihu chased them when we first came but never succeeded in nabbing one and decided it was better to not try again.

The camels walking by the entrance to our 'hole'.

Sunset over the sunflower fields.

The largest lake in the wilderness.

The desert on the north side of the Ulungur River; that's Mum in the distance.

Spring flowers.

A fossil collected in the wilderness. It's fairly clear that it's some sort of ancient organism; I tried to make a pendant out of it, but it looks awful.

I don't know how many times Mum and I got off the long-distance bus here. We'd wait for the connecting local bus, but we never knew when it would arrive, or if it would even come at all.

The winds would blow like mad through the greenery that hung on tight to the edge of the river.

Raggedy Saihu standing on her rear legs, her eyes looking off into the distance; I wonder what she sees.

Dusk over Akehala. This is where my mum ran her small grocery all those years.

ABOUT THE AUTHOR

Born in 1979 in Kuitun City, Xinjiang, Li Juan spent her formative years shuttling back and forth between Xinjiang and Sichuan as her parents were members of the Xinjiang Production and Construction Corps, an economic and paramilitary unit involved in agricultural reclamation projects. Her experiences among the herdsmen of Altay during this period have inspired much of her work. Her first collection of essays, titled *Nine Shapes of Snow*, was published in 1999, and this was followed by several more short essay anthologies and a trilogy of longer collections – *Distant Sunflower Fields*, *Winter Pasturelands* and *The Herd's Path* – on life in northern Xinjiang. She has also published a volume of poetry titled *The Quickly Departing Train*. Her works have gained wide acclaim in China and been translated into several languages, including French, Korean and Arabic. *Distant Sunflower Fields* is the first to be published in English.

ABOUT THE TRANSLATOR

Christopher Payne has co-translated the award-winning novels *Decoded* and *In the Dark* by Mai Jia, and along with his frequent collaborator, Olivia Milburn, he's also brought Jiang Zilong's magnum opus, *Empires of Dust*, to an English-language audience. Christopher holds a PhD in Chinese literature from the School of Oriental and African Studies at the University of London, and he has spent more than a decade teaching at postsecondary institutions, most notably Sungkyunkwan University in Seoul, South Korea, and The University of Manchester in the UK. In the autumn of 2019, he returned to his native Canada to become a full-time translator and continue to bring contemporary Chinese fiction to the world.